Systematic
Electronic
Diagnosis

D0835378

Systematic Electronic Fault Diagnosis

T. H. Wingate

B.Sc.
Instructor Lieutenant Commander,
Royal Navy

London
Sir Isaac Pitman & Sons Ltd.

First published 1968

SIR ISAAC PITMAN & SONS LTD.
Pitman House, Parker Street, Kingsway, London, W.C.2
The Pitman Press, Bath
Pitman House, Bouverie Street, Carlton, Melbourne
P.O. Box 7721 Johannesburg, Transvaal
P.O. Box 6038, Portal Street, Nairobi, Kenya

Associated Companies
PITMAN MEDICAL PUBLISHING COMPANY LTD.
46 Charlotte Street, London, W.1

PITMAN PUBLISHING CORPORATION
20 East 46th Street, New York, N.Y. 10017

SIR ISAAC PITMAN & SONS (CANADA) LTD.
Pitman House, 381-383 Church Street, Toronto

Made and printed in Great Britain by
Unwin Brothers Limited, Woking and London

Preface

The method of fault diagnosis taught in this program has been in use for some time, but is not widely known under the formalized principles given here. Indeed, many experienced workers will probably find that the method bears more than a passing resemblance to methods which they already employ. However, for the inexperienced worker, a set of guide-lines are necessary to enable fault finding to be carried out efficiently.

The method used here has been developed in the Royal Navy from original work done in the United States Navy, and now forms the basis of fault-finding teaching in the technical training establishment of the Royal Navy which has responsibility for this subject.

The material is presented in a Programmed Instruction format, and is a multiple-choice branching program in scrambled book form. It has been found that this method has many advantages, particularly in the field of self-instruction, and the author considers this to be the best vehicle for this work.

T.H.W.

Contents

Insets at end of book
    Valve Superhet Receiver Circuit
    Transistor Superhet Receiver Circuit
    Revision Flow Chart

Introduction

Program objectives
The overall objective of the program is to present a systematic and logical method in the technique of fault finding which can be applied to electronic equipments in general.

The examples used in the program are mainly concerned with the superhet receiver in valve and transistorized forms, and will thus tend to favour this type of equipment. However, these examples are only used to illustrate the program and it will be found that fault diagnosis on any electronic equipment will be improved by the use of this program.

On completion of the program, the student will have learnt the basic steps of the fault-finding method, and have discovered how to weld these steps into a composite method of fault diagnosis and repair. The actual method of fault diagnosis advised by this program can be found in the flow sheet or algorithm included at the end of the program.

Target population
Although this program is intended to be an aid to any person carrying out fault finding on any electronic equipment, it should prove particularly valuable for those taking the Radio and Television Servicing Examinations of the Radio Trades Examination Board.

Pre-knowledge required
The minimum knowledge required for entry to this program is a basic knowledge of the operation of a superhet receiver. It will be an advantage if the student is able to operate, and have experience of the use of, multimeters, oscilloscopes and signal generators. Any deeper knowledge than this limit will enhance the performance of the program. In particular, a knowledge of the theory of measurements will prove advantageous.

For the sections dealing with the transistorized superhet receiver, a working knowledge of transistors is required.

Evaluation
The testing of this program was successful, and on the basis of these tests was adopted as a standard work for the Royal Navy. For full details of the evaluation, turn to the next page.

Use of this program

This program is presented as an aid to the existing works on fault finding. The method taught here is a basic one, which can be applied to any equipment. For courses designed for particular types of equipment it will be necessary to supplement the program with specialized work on the equipment in question.

Time involved

As a program allows the student to proceed at his own pace, the time required for completion of this program will vary. It is suggested that the maximum time required will be in the region of eight hours, but that faster students may complete in four hours or less. This time will vary considerably with groups of differing ability, but should lie within these limits.

It is not envisaged that anyone will be required to work through the complete program without a break, and therefore the work has been divided into suitable sections. The break points between these sections consist of a series of progress tests and summaries on the section in question. These will enable the work to be divided into convenient time intervals.

Supplementary reading

In using this program to its best advantage, it will most probably be advisable to follow up this work with supplementary reading. A list of suggested reading is included at the end of this book. It is impossible to include all the works on this subject, especially on specific equipments, and no significance should be attached to the omission of any particular book.

Further exercises

It is recommended that the reader should attempt further exercises in fault-finding using the method advocated in this program, in order to consolidate the instructions given. Ideally these should be attempted under controlled laboratory conditions with an actual equipment. However, if this is not possible, an extremely good substitute is the series of fault-finding simulator sheets marketed by Printechnic under the title of Trainer-Tester Sheets. Time spent in these extra exercises will be amply rewarded by enhanced performance in fault finding.

Evaluation

This is a second-generation program from a program originally developed for the Royal Navy. It has been validated successfully and it is considered that the program is in a suitable state for immediate use.

The sample of trainees used for evaluation was one class of Leading Radio Electrical Mechanics, one class of Radio Mechanician Apprentices, two classes of Artificer Apprentices, and three classes of Radio Electrical Mechanics.

Method of Evaluation
The classes of Radio Electrical Mechanics, Radio Mechanician Apprentices, and Leading Radio Electrical Mechanics were each given one group of three faults prior to the program and one group of three faults after the program. The Artificer Apprentices were given two groups of three faults prior to the program and two groups of three faults after the program.

The evaluation carried out was based on measuring fault finding knowledge and capability before working through the program and comparing this with fault finding knowledge and capability after working through the program. The trainer test sheets were used for both purposes. It was not considered suitable to give the same faults before and after the program, and therefore compatible groups of faults were made up. For each fault, where a solution was found, five parameters of performance were measured. These were as follows:
  (1) The number of steps taken to cure the fault
  (2) The weighted score for these steps
  (3) The number of components replaced
  (4) The weighted score for components replaced
  (5) The total time taken to cure the fault.

Results Obtained
The results obtained are shown in the table overleaf:

Group	Number in group	Pre-test: total faults uncompleted (x)	Post-test: total faults uncompleted (y)	Overall percentage improvement $\left(\frac{x-y}{x}\right) \times 100$	Overall percentage decrease in time taken
Radio Mechanician Apprentices	23	20	5	75%	63%
Leading Radio Electrical Mechanics	17	5	0	100%	71%
Radio Electrical Mechanics	42	25	3	88%	51%
Artificer Apprentices	11	15	7	53%	18%

Conclusions

It is of interest to note that the Leading Radio Electrical Mechanics show the largest percentage increase in improvement and decrease in time taken. This group is the only one which had had extensive practice in fault finding as part of their duties prior to taking the course.

The Artificer Apprentices did not show a significant improvement in the number of steps and it is thought that the equipment and faults in question were probably not complicated enough for their standard. On the whole the result of this test showed a satisfactory improvement in fault finding performance.

The fault finding program has provided a significant increase in fault finding performance, particularly in respect of the time and effort spent in the fault repair, and this is due to instilling a logical standardized approach to the problem.

First of all you will be shown how to use this book.

If you are familiar with scrambled books you may wish to omit this section. If so, you may turn to Frame 7.

If you are not familiar with scrambled books, carry on with this frame.

The book is split into small units, called FRAMES.

There are one or more frames on each page. Each frame contains some information, and the main frames each have a question after this information. Read the information carefully and then attempt the question. When you have decided upon your answer look under the question where you will see several answers. Your answer should be one of those given. Beside this answer you will see a frame number. This is the frame which you should turn to, and there you will be able to follow up your answer to the question.

For example, here is a question on the information in this frame. What constitutes a main frame?

   A.   Information   *Frame 3*
   B.   Information and a question   *Frame 4*
   C.   Information, a question and answers   *Frame 5*

2

You should not have arrived on this frame.

Nowhere in the book have you been told to go to this frame.

Now go back to Frame 1 and use this scrambled book properly by only turning to frames as you are told in the text.

3

Your answer was that a main frame consists only of information. This is not correct.

You were told quite clearly that a main frame consisted of information, a question and answers. This was simply a fact which you did not learn properly. You do not need explanations as to why you are wrong; simply to be told of your mistake will suffice as the correction to this mistake.

If the question had been more difficult and you had needed more correction, then you could have worked through a small sequence of extra frames before carrying on with the main sequence.

Whatever correction you need at each question will be provided automatically, controlled by the answers you give to the questions on the main frames.

Now turn to *Frame 5*.

4

Your answer was that a main frame consists of information and a question. This is not correct.

You were told quite clearly that a main frame consisted of information, a question and answers. This was simply a fact which you did not learn properly. You do not need explanations as to why you are wrong; simply to be told of your mistake will suffice as the correction to this mistake.

If the question had been more difficult and you had needed more correction, then you could have worked through a small sequence of extra frames before carrying on with the main sequence.

Whatever correction you need at each question will be provided automatically, controlled by the answers you give to the questions on the main frames.

Now turn to *Frame 5*.

5

Your answer was correct when you said that each main frame consisted of information, a question and answers.

Each main frame will introduce a new piece of information, and you will be questioned on this in the frame. If you give the correct answer then you probably understood the information which you had been given in the frame. In this case you may move straight on to the next piece of information on the following main frame.

However, if you give an incorrect answer to the question then you did not fully understand the information given in the frame. This misunderstanding will be corrected before you are allowed to proceed. The correction will be made by routing you via a subsidiary frame, or by several subsidiary frames if your answer necessitated this.

To see how this happens, return to Frame 1 and try giving an incorrect answer to the question.

When you have done this, turn to *Frame 6*.

6

You should now see that your route through the frames will be determined by your answers to the questions. Correct answers indicate that you understand that particular topic and that you may go straight on. Incorrect answers indicate that you did not fully understand the topic and that this must be corrected before moving on.

You will not read every frame when you use this system, but the frames you read will be the ones which you require. It will therefore be necessary for you to turn from one frame to another, rather than to read the pages consecutively as in a normal book. It is of the utmost importance that you only turn to the frames as indicated, otherwise you will lose your route through the program and the sequence will lose continuity.

You will find your routing very easy to do as you work through the book, and it will happen to you automatically.

Now turn to *Frame 7*.

SYMPTOM ANALYSIS

This programmed text will teach you a general method of systematic fault finding which you will be able to apply to problems on any electronic equipment. However, this method of fault finding can be applied successfully to other situations and some of the more everyday aspects of these situations will be used as we are building up the method.

For example, here is a situation which occurs all too often. On attempting to drive away in your car, you find that the engine will not start.

What would be your first step to rectify this fault?

A. Grab a spanner and get under the bonnet   *Frame 10*
B. Get out and telephone a garage   *Frame 12*
C. Sit and think about what could be wrong   *Frame 14*

8

You said that the most important consideration with regard to the possible engine fault was the value of the tyre pressures. This is a fact concerning the car, but it is a fact which could have no possible bearing on the fault in the car, namely that the engine would not start.

Although as many facts, or symptoms, concerning the faulty equipment as possible are required, only those facts which have some bearing upon the actual fault in question are of real importance.

Of the three facts which you were given, the most important fact concerning the fault was whether or not the engine turned over. This has a direct bearing upon the fault.

Now turn to *Frame 11*.

Right. The one fact, whether or not the engine turned over, would most probably not be sufficient to isolate the exact fault.

In order to isolate the fault quickly and easily, as many symptoms as possible should be gathered together and made into a list. Of course, this list does not always need to be written down, but doing this would almost invariably help in the fault finding.

The symptoms of the engine fault would include such things as

whether the engine turned over or not
whether there was any petrol in the tank
whether the engine fired or not
whether the battery was flat or not.

These are all symptoms which we could determine without carrying out any large-scale checks. We could listen for the engine turning over and firing, we could check the petrol by inspecting the petrol gauge, and we could tell whether the battery was flat by testing the lights.

These TROUBLE SYMPTOMS could all have some bearing upon the possible fault, and to carry out fault finding in the most efficient way as many as possible of these symptoms should be gathered together.

When a list of all possible Trouble Symptoms has been made, do you think that

A. They should all be considered in turn? *Frame 19*
or
B. They should be considered together? *Frame 15*

10

You would grab a spanner and get under the bonnet.

It is possible that this move would find the fault quickly, but it is much more probable that you would not find the fault quickly and easily. This is not the correct move.

First of all you should sit and think about what could be wrong.

If you were a very experienced mechanic, or if the fault had occurred several times before, then you would probably be thinking about the fault so quickly that you would not notice the mental effort!

The amount of time which you need to spend will depend upon how experienced you are in fault finding, but this time will never be wasted.

Turn to *Frame 14.*

11

Whether or not the engine turned over is an important fact concerning the problem and you should notice this.

This fact is what is known as a SYMPTOM of the fault.

Would this one fact, or symptom, be sufficient to isolate the exact fault?

    A. Yes *Frame 13*
    B. No *Frame 9*

12

You would get out of the car and telephone a garage.

If you know nothing at all about a car then this would be a reasonable thing to do. But if you knew this little about a car then it is possible that you should not be driving it!

However, this was just an example. When we try examples on electronic equipment then you should have sufficient knowledge of electronics to enable you to carry out fault-finding procedures. In this case you should not get someone else to do your job for you, and the first step in your fault finding should be to sit and think about what could be wrong.

Turn to *Frame 14.*

13

This one fact, whether or not the engine turned over, might possibly tell us what the fault is likely to be but it is much more likely that your fault finding will be successful if you have as many facts, or symptoms, as possible.

Turn to *Frame 9.*

14

When the engine would not start you would sit and think about what could be wrong, which is quite correct.

However, aimless thinking will be of very little use. What is needed is to think logically and to sort out every fact which could have some bearing on the problem.

Which of the following considerations would have most bearing on the problem?

   A. What the tyre pressures were   *Frame 8*
   B. Whether or not the engine turned over   *Frame 11*
   C. If you should buy a new car   *Frame 16*

15

You were correct. Considering each Trouble Symptom in turn may tell us quite a lot about the possible fault, but considering all the symptoms together should give a much clearer picture of the fault. All of the symptoms should fit together, rather like a jig-saw puzzle.

This process of collective consideration is called ANALYSIS of the symptoms.

When a fault occurs, the first thing to do is to list all of the symptoms and tie them together logically to form a composite picture of the possible fault or condition.

This process is called SYMPTOM ANALYSIS, and should always be the first step carried out in logical, systematic fault finding.

For example, here is another everyday situation. Suppose that you develop a fault in yourself and you find that you have a pain in your ankle. You then go to see your doctor. He tries to find out as many symptoms as possible concerning the fault, the pain in the ankle.

The doctor finds out the following facts from you:

    (i) You also have a cold
   (ii) Your ankle only hurts when you put your weight on it
  (iii) You had too much to drink the night before.

Which of the above facts would be a symptom which the doctor would be interested in:

    A. (i)   *Frame 18*
    B. (ii) *Frame 20*
    C. (iii) *Frame 23*

16

You said that the most important consideration with regard to the possible engine fault was whether you should buy a new car. This is side-stepping the problem.

The most important consideration is to find the fault and to repair it, not just to replace the faulty item of equipment. The question asked which was the most important fact which would have some bearing on the problem and you did not answer the question properly. Let's have another try at the question.

Which of the following considerations would have most bearing on the problem of why the engine would not start?

    A. What the tyre pressures were *Frame 8*
    B. Whether or not the engine turned over *Frame 11*

17

Here is an example on a piece of electronic equipment.

You are given a valve radio receiver to service. The fault, you are told, is that the radio has a very low output when tuned to a particular station.

Which of the following would be part of your symptom analysis?

    A. Take out the valves and test in a valve-tester *Frame 21*
    B. Remove the chassis from the case and inspect it for burnt-out components, loose connexions and obvious faults *Frame 24*
    C. Tune the receiver to other stations to check the sound output *Frame 26*

18

The fact that you also have a cold is actually a symptom and the doctor would probably be interested in this fact. However, he would not be interested in this symptom as a way of determining exactly what is wrong with your ankle.

Although it is very important to collect as many symptoms as possible, those that can have no bearing on the fault you are immediately concerned with should be ignored. However, you will not always be able to tell whether the symptom is related or not and in this case it is best to consider *all* the symptoms.

Let us have another look at the question.

The doctor finds out the following facts from you:

    (i)   You had too much to drink the night before
   (ii) Your ankle only hurts when you put your weight on it.

Which of the above facts would be a symptom of the ankle pain which the doctor would be interested in:

    A.   (i)   *Frame 22*
    B. (ii)   *Frame 20*

19

Your answer was that all the symptoms should be considered in turn.

In many cases this would in fact enable you to find the fault as easily as possible, but you would be more certain of *always* finding the fault if you considered all the symptoms together, building up a picture of the possible fault condition.

Turn to *Frame 15.*

Right. If your ankle only hurts when you put your weight on it then this is a symptom of the fault which would interest the doctor. He then tries to find out as many other relevant symptoms as possible, and then carries out an analysis of the symptoms he has collected in an effort to determine the fault.

All of these symptoms must be very easily determined without the need for complicated tests and procedures.

Exactly the same concept held for the fault on the car. The symptoms had to be very easily and quickly determined. For example, the petrol gauge was inspected, the battery was checked by inspecting the lamps, and note was taken of whether the engine turned over or not.

You should listen, look, inspect meters, try the controls, paying particular attention to any immediately obvious facts whatever the fault-finding situation.

Exactly the same technique holds good for fault finding in electronic equipment. The first step, before any testing, is to carry out SYMPTOM ANALYSIS. It is extremely important that this is the first step to be carried out in a fault-finding situation.

Now to try an example on a piece of electronic equipment.

Turn to *Frame 17.*

21

You said that part of your symptom analysis of the fault on the radio receiver would be to take out all the valves and test them in a valve-tester.

Testing valves is a standard fault-finding procedure but it should never be used at this stage of the problem.

As the fault is not necessarily in a valve at all, then testing all the valves at this stage would be a complete waste of time.

In any case, you should never have to test all the valves in a set. Normally there will only be a few valves, but a more complicated piece of equipment could contain a very large number, and to test all of these could take a very long time with no guarantee of finding the fault.

There should be no complicated tests in symptom analysis.

Try the question again.

Turn to *Frame 17.*

22

The fact that you had too much to drink the night before might have been the *cause* of the pain in your ankle, but it is not a *symptom.*

A symptom is a fact concerning the effects of the fault which should tell you something about the fault itself.

Remember this and then have another look at the question.

Turn to *Frame 18.*

23

The fact that you had too much to drink the night before might have been the *cause* of the pain in your ankle, but it is not a *symptom*.

A symptom is a fact concerning the effects of the fault which should tell you something about the actual fault.

Remember this and then have another look at the question.

Turn to *Frame 15*.

24

You said that part of your symptom analysis of the fault on the radio receiver would be to remove the chassis from the case and inspect it for burnt-out components, loose connexions and obvious faults.

This is a good move but *not* at this stage. During symptom analysis your inspection should be confined to the outside of the set. You may find something even more obvious without even removing the case. Inspection inside the receiver should only be carried out after carrying out as much symptom analysis as possible.

If you look at the question again you should be able to find some further symptom analysis which you could carry out before this inspection inside the case.

Turn to *Frame 17*.

25

If you arrived at this frame, you must either be using the book incorrectly, or you have decided to try and ignore the routing provided.

If you did not follow the routing correctly, turn to *Frame 7* and start the program again.

If you did not properly understand how to use this program, turn to *Frame 1* and revise the method of routing through this scrambled program.

26

Yes. If you tuned in to other stations to check their output you would be carrying out symptom analysis on the fault. The information which you could obtain in this way could give you a great deal of information about the possible fault. Also this information could be obtained very easily and quickly.

For example, the low sound output might be found to be only at one end of the frequency range of the receiver, it might be found to be over the entire frequency range, or the receiver might be found to be giving a low sound output only at one particular frequency. All of the information which you obtain in this way will be useful in your efforts to find the fault.

When you consider all of this information collectively, then you are carrying out symptom analysis, the first step in efficient fault finding.

If this symptom analysis is carried out correctly, it can be of great assistance in isolating the area of the fault as quickly as possible; indeed in some cases efficient symptom analysis should be able to determine the exact fault.

Let's see if we can show this to you.

Turn to *Frame 27*.

You will now be given a simple electrical circuit and we will use this circuit to see how symptom analysis can aid fault finding in electrical circuits.

As this circuit will be used for several frames, it will be necessary for you to make a copy of the circuit.

Then turn to *Frame 28*.

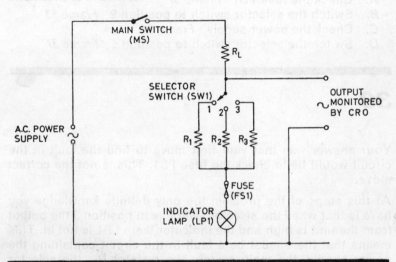

28

The circuit represents a simplified bench supply, giving three switched a.c. outputs. These outputs are monitored with an oscilloscope.

For our purposes, consider that the fuse FS1 and the indicator lamp LP1 have a large power rating so that they should be protected from the failure of a component in the power supply itself, their main function being a safeguard against failure in the circuit connected to the power supply.

Now turn to *Frame 29*.

29

The fault on this circuit is as follows.

When the selector switch SW1 is in position 3, the output is higher than its normal value and the indicator lamp LP1 is not lit.

What should be the first move in your fault-finding procedure?

A. Check the fuse FS1   *Frame 31*
B. Switch the selector switch to position 2   *Frame 33*
C. Check the power supply   *Frame 35*
D. Switch the selector switch to position 1   *Frame 37*

30

Your answer was that your first move to find the fault in the circuit would be to check the fuse FS1. This is not the correct move.

At this stage of the problem the only definite knowledge you have is that when the selector switch is in position 3 the output from the unit is high and the indicator lamp LP1 is not lit. This means that there must be a fault in the circuit containing the power supply, the main switch, the resistor R_L, the selector switch SW1, the resistor R_3, the fuse FS1 and the indicator lamp LP1. There are seven components in this circuit and we should not attempt to check individual components until we are more certain of the fault.

In fact a faulty fuse could be the cause of the symptoms we have already been given, but it is not the only possible cause.

There is another step which we could take and which would help to isolate the fault to a smaller number of components.

If you have another look at the question you should be able to decide upon this step.

Turn to the question on *Frame 39*.

Your answer was that your first move to find the fault in the circuit would be to check the fuse FS1. This is not the correct move.

At this stage in the problem the only definite knowledge you have is that when the selector switch SW1 is in position 3 the output from the unit is high and the indicator lamp LP1 is not lit. This means that there must be a fault in the circuit containing the power supply, the main switch, the resistor R_L, the selector switch SW1, the resistor R_3, the fuse FS1 and the indicator lamp LP1. There are seven components in this circuit and we should not attempt to check individual components until we are more certain of the fault.

In fact a faulty fuse could be the cause of the symptoms we already have been given, but it is not the only possible cause.

There is another step which we could take and which would help to isolate the fault to a smaller number of components.

If you have another look at the question you should be able to decide upon this step.

Turn to the question on *Frame 29*.

32

When the selector switch SW1 was in position 3 and the output was high there could have been several faulty components. By switching to position 2 or 1 and observing the symptoms obtained by this move, you should have been able to narrow the faulty area. In fact you should be able to tell if the fault lies in the part of the circuit common to all three outputs, or in the part of the circuit which is only switched in for one of the outputs.

The information obtained from this move is as follows:

When the selector switch was in position 2 the output was normal.

When the selector switch was in position 1 the output was normal.

Do you now have sufficient information to enable you to definitely isolate the fault to a small area?

A. No *Frame 40*
B. Yes *Frame 42*
C. I don't know *Frame 44*

33

Correct. The quickest, simplest and correct move would be to switch the selector switch SW1 to position 2. This provides the quickest method of obtaining more symptoms concerning the fault.

Remember that you should always obtain as many symptoms as possible before attempting any diagnosis of the fault.

Now turn to *Frame 32*.

34

By considering the information we have gained so far in this problem you should be able to isolate the fault to a small area of the circuit. Here is the information you have been given.

1. Output 3 is high but output 1 and output 2 are normal. Therefore the fault must lie in the part of the circuit only used for output 3, i.e. position 3 of the selector switch SW1, or the resistor R_3.

2. The indicator lamp LP1 lights in position 1 and in position 2 of the selector switch, but not in position 3. Therefore there must be no current through the indicator lamp when the selector switch is in position 3, and this should be caused by an open circuit between position 3 of the selector switch and the indicator lamp through R_3.

The fault could be a dry joint, a faulty switch, or a faulty resistor. Of these three the most likely is a faulty resistor. This could be verified by carrying out further checks on the circuit, but by carrying out symptom analysis to its fullest extent the number of components needing test has been very much reduced.

Turn to *Frame 42*.

Turn to *Frame 42*.

35

Your answer was that your first move to find the fault in the circuit would be to check the power supply. This is not the correct move.

It is possible that a high value of the power supply could explain the symptom of the high output. However, this fault could not explain the other symptom which you were given. This second symptom was that the indicator lamp LP1 did not light.

You only considered one symptom to arrive at your diagnosis of the fault. To carry out fault finding correctly you must consider every available symptom before making a diagnosis. This means not only considering the symptoms you are given, but also obtaining as many other symptoms as possible.

Keeping this in mind, have another look at the question.

Turn to the question on *Frame 39*.

Turn to the question on *Frame 39*.

36

Now to see if you correctly isolated the probable fault.

Which component is most likely to be at fault?

- A. Fuse FS1 is ruptured   *Frame 38*
- B. Resistor R_3 has too high a value   *Frame 41*
- C. Switch SW1 is not making contact in position 3   *Frame 43*

37

Right. Switching the selector switch SW1 to position 1 would be a very quick and easy means of gathering more symptoms concerning the fault.

However, to get to position 1 of the selector switch, you would have to go through position 2. In this case it would be just as easy to leave the switch in position 2 rather than go on to position 1 because both positions would give the same information.

Switching to either of these two positions would be correct since it would be a very quick and easy method of gathering more symptoms.

Now turn to *Frame 33*.

38

You said that the most likely component to be at fault was the fuse FS1. This is not correct.

You did not pay sufficient attention to the symptoms which were given to you. When the switch was in position 1 and 2, then the indicator lamp LP1 lit. Therefore the fuse FS1 must be intact and there is no point in testing it. The reason for carrying out symptom analysis is to eliminate unnecessary tests.

Turn to *Frame 36*.

39

Let's try this problem again.

You were told that when the selector switch SW1 is in position 3, the output is higher than its normal value and the indicator lamp LP1 is not lit.

What should be the first move in your fault-finding procedure?

- A. Switch the selector switch to position 2 *Frame 33*
- B. Check the fuse FS1 *Frame 30*
- C. Switch the selector switch to position 1 *Frame 37*

40

You said that you did not have sufficient information to isolate the fault to a very small area. In fact you do now have sufficient information.

If you turn to *Frame 34* you will see how the fault can be isolated.

41

You said that the most likely component to be at fault was resistor R_3, the resistance being too high.

This is not correct.

You did not pay sufficient attention to the symptoms which were given to you. When output 3 was monitored it was found to be high, and the indicator lamp was not lit. This means that there was probably no current through the indicator lamp. If the resistor R_3 was simply too high a value then there would be some current through the indicator lamp, even if it were very small, and some response should be obtained from the indicator lamp.

Return to *Frame 36* and have another attempt at the question.

42

Right. You should now have a fairly good idea of the actual fault, and you should be certain that you can isolate the fault to a small area.

Turn to *Frame 36* to see if you thought this out correctly.

43

Correct. The faulty component is most likely to be an open circuit on position 3 of the selector switch. It could also be resistor R_3 on open circuit.

This fault was isolated simply by switching to output 1 and output 2 and observing the symptoms. By correctly considering these symptoms an accurate forecast of the fault could be made, eliminating the need for a series of tests.

This was a very simple example but it underlines the usefulness of correct symptom analysis. The more complicated the fault-finding problem, the more help can be obtained from symptom analysis. This must always be the first step in your fault-finding method, and time and effort spent in carrying out symptom analysis can never be wasted.

Turn to *Frame 45*.

44

You said that you do not know if you have enough information to isolate the fault to a very small area of the circuit.

You should know enough about electrical circuits to enable you to isolate the fault to a small area. However, if you turn to *Frame 34* you will see how this can be done.

45

Now we can have a look at a simple example of how symptom analysis can help in a fault-finding problem on a simplified superhet receiver. For this a full circuit diagram is not required, and a block diagram of the equipment is all that is necessary in the early stages of fault finding.

The block diagram below is of a basic superhet receiver designed to give reception on three wavebands: short wave, medium wave, and long wave. This is not meant to be any particular radio receiver as the method which you are being taught here can be applied to any equipment.

Make a copy of this diagram since you will need to use it for several frames and this will save you constantly turning back to this frame. Having done this, turn to *Frame 46*.

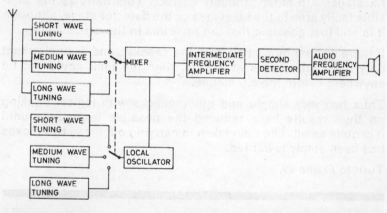

46

When the receiver is tuned to a known signal, in the long waveband, there is no sound output from the loudspeaker apart from a very low hum.

What should be the first step in your fault-finding procedure?

A. Switch to another waveband and tune to another known signal *Frame 48*
B. Check the a.f. stages by injecting a test signal *Frame 50*
C. Check the h.t. supply from the rectifier stage *Frame 52*

Listening for hum in the speaker of a radio receiver is a correct part of symptom analysis and should give valuable information on the fault. If there is a hum then it usually means that the a.f. stages, the speaker and the power supply from the rectifier are correct. An experienced technician would probably be able to determine more about the fault in some cases by the exact type of hum present in the receiver. This cannot be taught here, but will be gained with experience.

Assuming that there was the normal hum from the speaker to be expected with that particular radio receiver, then the a.f. stages, the speaker and the h.t. supply are most probably correct. The previous step of symptom analysis showed that since there was no output on any of the three wavebands the r.f. stages are most probably correct. This narrows the possible faulty area to the i.f. stages or the detector stage, although it is still just possible that the fault lies in the aerial.

If there was no hum at all from the speaker, and assuming that only one fault occurs at a time, then the fault could not lie anywhere before the a.f. stages.

Thus two very simple and quick checks with logical thinking on their results have reduced the possible faulty area until it is quite small. The time taken in carrying out these two moves has been amply rewarded.

Turn to *Frame 49*.

You have been told so far that symptom analysis of the faulty equipment must be the first step in efficient fault finding, and you applied this correctly. By switching to another waveband and tuning to another known signal, more relevant information concerning the fault would be discovered.

If a normal output were obtained from either of the other two wavebands, then the fault must lie in the circuits only concerned with the long waveband. This would immediately narrow the possible faulty area a great deal.

However, let us consider that there is still no output from any of the three wavebands.

What should be the next step in your fault-finding procedure?

A. Connect another speaker   *Frame 51*
B. Listen for hum in the loudspeaker   *Frame 53*
C. Check the aerial for possible faults   *Frame 55*

In general, when carrying out symptom analysis, how many symptoms would be required?

A. One symptom   *Frame 56*
B. Two symptoms   *Frame 58*
C. As many symptoms as you could find   *Frame 60*

50

When there was no sound output from the radio receiver when it was switched to the long waveband, you said that your first move would be to check the a.f. stages by injecting a test signal.

This is not correct. You do not know that the fault lies in the a.f. stages and therefore you should not carry out tests on these stages at this point. This test would involve the use of special test equipment and would take several minutes to carry out. As the fault is not definitely in these stages, this test could be a complete waste of time.

Remember that the first step in fault finding should be to carry out as much symptom analysis as possible. Have another look at the question given below.

When the receiver is tuned to a known signal, in the long waveband, there is no sound output from the loudspeaker apart from a very low hum.

What should be the first step in your fault-finding procedure?

A. Check the h.t. supply from the rectifier stage *Frame 54*
B. Switch to another waveband and tune to another known signal *Frame 48*

51

When it was found that there was no output from the speaker on any of the three wavebands, you said that the next step should be to connect another speaker to check if this is the fault. This is not the correct move.

Connecting another speaker might be an easy step to carry out if the set has a plug-in speaker and a spare is available. However, it is more likely that you would have to remove the receiver from its case, dismantle the speaker, unsolder the leads, mount a new speaker, and resolder the leads. This is going to take quite a while and will almost certainly not help to find the fault as you are not yet certain of the faulty area.

You should not replace components until you are certain that they are faulty, as replacing components always takes a comparatively long time and is very wasteful.

Remember that you should obtain as many symptoms of the fault as possible before going any further. These symptoms must be easily and quickly obtained, and should not involve the use of test equipment or the replacing of components.

Have another look at the question.

Turn to *Frame 48*.

52

When there was no sound output from the radio receiver when it was switched to the long waveband, you said that your first move would be to check the h.t. supply from the rectifier stage.

This is not correct. You do not know that the fault definitely lies in the rectifier stage and therefore you should not carry out this test at the present point in your fault-finding procedure. As the fault is not definitely in this stage this test could be a complete waste of time.

Remember that the first step in fault finding should be to carry out as much symptom analysis as possible. Have another look at the question given below.

When the receiver is tuned to a known signal, in the long waveband, there is no sound output from the loudspeaker apart from a very low hum.

What should be the first step in your fault-finding procedure?

   A. Switch to another waveband and tune to another known signal *Frame 48*

   B. Check the a.f. stages by injecting a test signal *Frame 54*

53

Right. You should carry on with symptom analysis as much as possible before carrying out any tests. Your answer of listening at the speaker for hum was correct. This is further symptom analysis which will give further information concerning the possible fault. In changing the speaker or checking the aerial you would only be eliminating one component from the possible faults. This checking of individual components must not be carried out until the final stages of fault finding.

The two steps of symptom analysis carried out so far would only take seconds to carry out in practice and would give much valuable information. In general, this is true of all good symptom analysis. The time it will take will be very small and will save large amounts of time taken in actual tests.

Turn to *Frame 47*.

54

You are not carrying out the method you have been taught which involves using as much symptom analysis as possible. You have twice tried to carry out a special test on a specific part of the circuit when you do not know definitely that the fault lies in these stages. There is a very easy and quick step which will enable you to carry out more symptom analysis and which will help you to isolate the fault to a certain part of the circuit before you need to carry out any tests at all.

This correct step should be to switch the receiver to another waveband, tune to a known signal, and observe the output from the speaker. This will show whether the fault lies in the r.f. stages or after the r.f. stages, and it will only take a very short while to carry out.

In every fault-finding problem, ALWAYS obtain as many symptoms as possible and consider them all logically to enable you to make an estimate of the fault, before carrying out any special tests.

Turn to *Frame 48*.

55

When it was found that there was no output from the speaker on any of the three wavebands, you said that the next step should be to check the aerial. This is not correct.

Even if this test could be carried out easily and quickly it will not provide any new information about the fault, except in the unlikely chance that the aerial is the faulty component. If the aerial were found to be working correctly then the fault could still be anywhere in the set. Moreover, you should be carrying out your tests on this with an injected signal, and this should not be done at this stage.

Remember that you should obtain as many symptoms of the fault as possible before going any further. These symptoms must be easily and quickly obtained, and should not involve the use of test equipment or the replacing of components.

Have another look at the question.

Turn to *Frame 48*.

56

One symptom might give us all the information we require in order to isolate the fault, but we should be very lucky indeed if this happened.

We will usually need several symptoms in order to gain much knowledge of the fault, and in fact it is always best to obtain as many symptoms as possible, even though one or two of these might not be needed. This will not be wasting time as all symptoms should be very quick and easy to obtain.

The more symptoms obtained, the easier it will be to isolate the fault.

Turn to *Frame 60*.

57

The symptoms which are immediately apparent might be sufficient to isolate the fault, but usually as many symptoms as possible will be required. In order to be certain, always obtain as many symptoms as possible, both those symptoms which are immediately apparent and those symptoms which have to be discovered.

Turn to *Frame 62*.

58

Two symptoms might give us all the information we require in order to isolate the fault, but we should be lucky if this happened.

We will usually need several symptoms in order to gain much knowledge of the fault, and in fact it is always best to obtain as many symptoms as possible even though one or two of these might not be needed. This will not be wasting time as all symptoms should be very quick and easy to obtain.

The more symptoms obtained, the easier it will be to isolate the fault.

Turn to *Frame 60*.

59

Other useful symptoms could very easily and quickly be found by operating the controls of the receiver or other equipment. However, be careful not to spend too long aimlessly altering controls which are not going to provide you with useful information. In certain cases there may be built-in test equipment, and in this case any results from this equipment should be included in the symptom analysis.

Always obtain as many symptoms as possible and then consider them in a logical way in order to obtain as much information about the fault as can be obtained easily, without carrying out specific tests.

However, no amount of symptom analysis will help you if you do not properly understand the basic electronic theory concerning your equipment and the principles involved. Never try to fault find on an equipment until you have this knowledge.

Symptom analysis should always save you time and effort.

It should make your task easier and make you more efficient.

Turn to *Frame 61*.

60

Correct. You should always try to find as many symptoms as possible.

In some cases this may give you too many symptoms. However, the symptoms are found so easily and quickly, and considering them correctly in order to make an estimate of the fault saves so much time that the extra time spent in finding one or two surplus symptoms will not affect the total time spent in fault finding. Too many symptoms are far better than too few.

When you are collecting these symptoms should you

A. Only look at those symptoms which are immediately apparent? *Frame 57*

or

B. Try to find other symptoms which are easily found as well as the symptoms which are immediately apparent? *Frame 62*

61

Sometimes you will come across an equipment which is not all in one unit. For example, a stereo system could consist of a control unit with associated amplifier units, tape deck, tuner and turntable. In this case your symptom analysis will have to be modified to suit the new circumstances.

When an equipment is separated into more than one unit, symptom analysis is of prime importance. A large amount of time could be wasted by investigating the incorrect unit instead of finding the faulty unit first of all.

For example, suppose that a stereo equipment of the type described above is brought to you with a fault. What should be your first move in finding the fault?

   A. Perform symptom analysis on each unit in turn until the faulty stage is found   *Frame 63*
   B. Perform symptom analysis on the complete system until the faulty unit is found   *Frame 66*

62

Correct. Several important symptoms would probably be found if you tried to obtain symptoms besides those which were immediately apparent. Remember, however, that these symptoms must not take very long to discover.

How should these other symptoms be obtained?

   A. By operating the controls   *Frame 59*
   B. By injecting test signals   *Frame 64*
   C. By monitoring the various outputs   *Frame 65*

63

You said that in a multi-unit equipment which had developed a fault, your first move in finding the fault would be to carry out symptom analysis on each unit in turn until the faulty stage was found. This is not correct.

A large amount of valuable time could be lost carrying out this move. You would be lucky if you started on the unit which contained the fault, and in most cases several units would be checked before finding the faulty unit. All of this time would be wasted.

The first move should be to carry out symptom analysis on the complete system in an attempt to isolate the faulty unit. Then, and only then, should symptom analysis be carried out on the single faulty unit to determine the faulty stage within the unit.

Turn to *Frame 66*.

64

You said that you would obtain further symptoms by injecting test signals. To do this you would need to use special test equipment and probably you would need to dismantle the receiver to some extent. This could take quite a long time to carry out. Of course you would be gaining some new information on the fault which would most probably be useful in isolating the fault, but you would not be carrying out symptom analysis; and you would most probably be taking longer to find the fault than someone who was carrying out symptom analysis correctly.

As many symptoms as possible must be obtained before any specialized tests are carried out.

Have another attempt at the question.

Turn to *Frame 62*.

65

You said that you would obtain further symptoms by monitoring the outputs. To do this you would need to use special test equipment and probably you would need to dismantle the receiver to some extent. This could take quite a long time to carry out.

Monitoring the outputs might actually give valuable information on the fault, but should not be carried out at this stage. When you listened for hum in the speaker in an earlier move, you monitored the output sufficiently well for our purposes at this stage.

As many symptoms as possible must be obtained before any specialized tests are carried out.

Have another attempt at the question.

Turn to *Frame 62*.

66

Correct. The first move in fault finding on a multi-unit equipment should be to carry out symptom analysis on the complete equipment to determine the faulty unit. Then symptom analysis should be carried out on the faulty unit to determine the faulty stage in that unit.

Now turn to the next page for a review of this section.

Review of Symptom Analysis

The first step in logical fault finding should be to carry out SYMPTOM ANALYSIS.

All relevant symptoms should be considered collectively, both immediately apparent symptoms and induced symptoms.

Immediately apparent symptoms will be obtained by checking the output, and noting any built-in monitor lamps, test gear, and any other such items. Induced symptoms will be obtained by operating whatever controls are available.

These symptoms should be very easily and quickly obtained, and should be considered in a logical way to obtain as much information about the fault as can easily be obtained without carrying out specific tests.

The purpose of symptom analysis is to attempt to narrow the possible faulty area as much as possible without the need for specific tests and test equipment.

In a multi-unit equipment, carry out symptom analysis on the equipment as a whole and attempt to isolate the fault to one unit. If this can be done then carry out symptom analysis on the faulty unit in an attempt to further isolate the fault.

No amount of symptom analysis will help you if you do not properly understand both the basic electronic theory concerning the equipment and the principles involved. Never try to fault find on an equipment until you have this knowledge.

Symptom analysis should always save you time and effort.

It should make your task easier, and make you more efficient.

Now turn to the next page for the section test.

Test 1

Write down the answers to the following questions.

1. What is the name of the first step in logical fault finding?
2. How many symptoms should you try to obtain in this step?
3. How long should it take you to obtain these symptoms?
4. Which items of test gear will be required for this step?
5. What is the difference between immediately apparent symptoms and induced symptoms?
6. How is symptom analysis applied to a multi-unit equipment?
7. How does the correct application of symptom analysis depend upon sound electronic theory?
8. A radio receiver is only giving a low hum, no signals being apparent. Where is the fault most likely to lie?
9. A radio receiver has very variable gain over the whole waveband. Where is the fault most likely to lie?
10. A radio receiver has a lot of noise present in the output. Where is the fault most likely to lie?

When you have written down the answers to these questions, turn to page *A* at the end of the book.

67
EQUIPMENT INSPECTION

When no further information concerning the fault can be found by symptom analysis, then fault finding must be pursued by other means. To investigate the step in fault finding after symptom analysis let us consider the very first example given, that of the car which would not start.

Let us suppose that when we carried out symptom analysis on the car fault we found that the engine turned over but did not fire, and that there was petrol present in the tank. There was no need in this case to check whether the battery was in order since it must be satisfactory to turn the engine in the correct way. Considering these symptoms it is reasonable to suppose that the fault is either that there is no petrol actually reaching the engine, or that there is no spark at the sparking plugs. All this could be determined whilst still sitting in the car, but now a new step has to be taken. What should the next step be?

A. An attempt should be made to push-start *Frame 69*
B. A quick test should be carried out to check if there was a spark at the sparking plugs *Frame 71*
C. An inspection of the engine should be carried out *Frame 73*

68

In the case of the engine fault, we have seen that an inspection of the equipment would be very easy and should only take a short while. Now for another example.

The second example you were given in the first section was when you went to the doctor with a pain in your ankle. His first step in determining the cause of this pain was to gather as many symptoms as possible and to consider them collectively. This he did by asking you questions about the pain.

What, in your opinion, would be the doctor's next step in determining the cause of the pain in your ankle?

A. Send you to the local hospital for an X-ray *Frame 70*
B. Inspect the ankle for obvious signs of damage *Frame 72*
C. Determine the area of the pain by pressing at various points on the ankle *Frame 74*

69

Your answer was that you would now try to push-start the car. This is not correct.

This move might possibly start the engine, but more probably the engine would still not start. The symptom analysis showed that there was petrol in the tank and that there was sufficient charge in the battery to turn the engine. However, we said earlier that the battery was able to turn the engine in the correct way, and we should assume from this that there is sufficient charge in the battery both to turn the engine and to supply a spark. In this case attempting to push-start the car engine could show a nil return for a large amount of effort.

Always try the easiest move first.

Return to *Frame 67* and attempt the question again.

70

Your answer was that the doctor would now send you to the local hospital for an X-ray. In fact he would not do this until he had ascertained some further information on the fault, the pain in your ankle. If the pain was due to an infected cut then he would be wasting his time and the hospital's time by sending you for an X-ray. Before going to this extreme the doctor would carry out another simple move to give him more information on the pain in your ankle.

Think very carefully of this move and then turn to *Frame 68* and try the question again.

71

Your answer was that you would now carry out a test on the engine to check if there was a spark at the sparking plugs. This is not correct.

This might possibly find the fault immediately, but you are not yet certain that the sparking plugs are the source of the trouble. Before carrying out detailed tests on individual components you should be certain that they are the components at fault.

Always try to find out as much information as possible before making an estimate of the fault.

Return to *Frame 67* and attempt the question again.

72

Correct. The next move that the doctor would make in finding the cause of the pain in your ankle would be to *look* at your ankle. A doctor is taught to look before touching. You must always do the same. Do not touch parts of an equipment until you have looked closely at them.

In the case of the pain in your ankle, the doctor might find an obvious cause of the pain. In an extreme case this could be a sliver of bone protruding through the flesh, or it could be something more usual such as discoloration, swelling, an insect bite, cut, abrasion, or any of the other many possible causes. All of these would be easily and quickly discernible.

Turn to *Frame 75*.

73

Your answer was that an inspection of the engine should be carried out. This is correct. If symptom analysis had not provided an immediate solution then an inspection of the equipment should be the next step.

In this inspection you should be looking for obvious faults and no tests should be carried out. All of the senses should be used in this inspection, attempting to find anything unusual. The first move should be to look at the equipment, but you should also notice any unusual smells and try by touch to check for any loose leads. You might also hear an unusual noise.

The result of these investigations should uncover such faults as a petrol leak found by smell or hearing the petrol escaping, and finding a loose lead to the distributor from the coil by looking or by pulling the lead.

Any obvious fault such as these should be found by an inspection of the faulty equipment, and this inspection should only take a very short while, a few minutes at the most.

Turn to *Frame 68*.

74

Your answer was that the doctor would now determine the area of the pain by pressing at various points on the ankle. This is not correct. The doctor would never touch your ankle until he had done something else, just as you should never touch an electrical equipment until you have carried out a previous move.

Think very carefully of what this move could be and then turn to *Frame 68* and try the question again.

75

You should now be becoming familiar with the process of equipment inspection, so let's move on to an example on a piece of electronic equipment.

In the first section you were given a valve radio receiver to service. The fault was that the radio has a very low output when tuned to a particular station. As part of your symptom analysis you tuned to other stations and compared the sound output at each. You could also try the effect of other controls, such as the gain control.

When you have carried out as much symptom analysis as possible then the next step should be to perform equipment inspection on the faulty electronic equipment, in the same way as you should inspect the car engine and the doctor should inspect your ankle.

Turn to *Frame 76*.

76

Right. For the electronic equipment the second step in fault finding would be exactly the same type of step as fault finding on a car engine or on your ankle. This second step is to carry out an inspection of the equipment.

The first step in fault finding is symptom analysis.

The second step in fault finding is EQUIPMENT INSPECTION.

When carrying out equipment inspection on a piece of electronic equipment, which of the following faults would you expect to find?

    A.   A burnt-out resistor   *Frame 78*
    B.   A valve producing low gain   *Frame 80*
    C.   A capacitor on short circuit   *Frame 82*

77

Sometimes you will be able to tell by touching a component if it is overheating, or if it is not hot when it is supposed to be. When touching components you must take great care. Apart from the possibility of being slightly burnt by an overheated component, you may possible be touching a component which is normally safe but because of the fault is carrying a dangerous potential.

An example on equipment inspection is that you suspect a valve heater is burned out. What would you expect to see?

A. A bright glow *Frame 79*
B. No glow at all *Frame 81*
C. A blue flickering light *Frame 83*

78

You said that the fault you were most likely to find by equipment inspection from the list given was a burnt-out resistor. This is correct.

There are many possible faults in an electronic equipment which will give no indication of their presence when equipment inspection is carried out. The purpose of equipment inspection in an electronic equipment is to find obvious faults, ones which can be found easily, directly and quickly. There are, however, many occasions when the fault is something which can be found by this process and amongst these faults are such things as a burnt-out resistor, loose plugs, loose switches, unlit valves, melted pitch on a transformer or other component, arcing, damaged cable or broken wires, and many others with which you should be familiar.

Turn to *Frame 77.*

79

You said that if a valve heater was burned out you would expect to see a bright glow in the valve. This is not correct. If the valve heater was burned out then you would not expect to see any glow at all in the valve. You were not thinking clearly when you gave this answer.

Turn to *Frame 81*.

80

No, you could not detect a valve producing low gain by carrying out equipment inspection. This should be obvious from your electronic knowledge. You could not have been thinking very carefully. In fault finding cloar and logical thinking backed up by good technical knowledge of theory is required.

Turn to *Frame 76* and try the question again.

81

Correct. If the valve heater was burned out you would not expect to see any glow at all in the valve.

However, the valve may be one which is enclosed in a metal case and then you could not tell by sight whether the heater was lit or not.

In this case how could you tell whether the heater was burned out?

A. By touching the valve and testing temperature   *Frame 84*
B. By removing the valve and testing it in a valve tester *Frame 86*
C. By measuring the voltage across the heater pins on the valve base   *Frame 88*

82

No, you could not detect a capacitor on short circuit by carrying out equipment inspection. This should be obvious from your electronic knowledge. You could not have been thinking very carefully. In fault finding clear and logical thinking backed up by good technical knowledge of theory is required.

Turn to *Frame 76* and try the question again.

83

You said that if a valve heater was burned out you would expect to see a blue flickering light in the valve. This is not correct. You should not expect to see this in a normal valve working correctly, or not working at all. This type of result might be given by a stabilizer valve working normally, but you were trying to establish whether or not the heater of a normal valve was burned out. You were not thinking clearly when you gave this answer. Now try the question again, thinking very carefully before you give an answer.

Turn to *Frame 77*.

84

Correct. By touching the valve you would be able to tell if it **were** hot or not and this would give you information on the operation of the valve. Testing the valve in a valve tester, or measuring the voltage across the heater pins on the valve base, would each show exactly whether or not the heater was operating correctly. However, these are both special tests and at this stage in the fault-finding procedure, i.e. equipment inspection, no tests should be carried out. Further information on the fault is being sought by simple inspection of the equipment.

Now for another aspect of equipment inspection. Suppose that in a high voltage equipment arcing was occurring as part of the fault. This could be seen, heard, and also observed by smell. The smell of arcing is the smell of ozone which is produced when a spark passes through air. The same smell may be detected near the commutator of a motor or generator.

This one type of fault can, then, be detected by using more than one sense. In fact, in all of your equipment inspection you should be using all of your senses, looking, listening, smelling and touching, if it is considered safe. All of these investigations should only take a short while. They should be very easy to carry out and should not involve the use of special tests. This is the second step in the fault-finding method, equipment inspection.

Turn to *Frame 85.*

85

Certain specialized equipments consist of several separate units. We have already used the example of a stereo system equipped with tape deck, record player, tuner, amplifiers and control unit.

In this case, where would you first carry out equipment inspection?

In the first unit of the equipment *Frame 87*
B. On the external parts of each unit and on the inter-unit connexions *Frame 89*

86

You said that you would tell whether or not the heater was burnt out by removing the valve and testing it in a valve tester. This would determine definitely if the valve heater was intact or not, but would involve a special test, taking several minutes, and this should not be done at this stage of fault finding. There is an easier way of making a first estimate of whether the heater is functioning correctly.

Now try the question again, thinking very carefully before you give an answer.

Turn to *Frame 81*.

87

In the case of a multi-unit equipment, inspection on the first unit should not be carried out as the first step in fault finding unless it is definitely the faulty unit. You should first of all carry out an inspection on the external parts of each unit and on the inter-unit connexions.

Turn to *Frame 89*.

88

You said that you would tell whether or not the heater was burnt out by measuring the voltage across the heater pins on the valve base. This would definitely determine whether the heater was receiving the correct voltage to enable it to operate correctly, but this test would not be of help at this stage and, in any case, specific tests should not be carried out at this stage of fault finding. There is an easier way of making a first estimate of whether the heater is functioning correctly.

Now try the question again, thinking very carefully before you give an answer.

Turn to *Frame 81*.

89

Correct. In multi-unit equipment you should first inspect the exterior of the units and the inter-unit connexions.

When the faulty unit has previously been isolated by symptom analysis then equipment inspection could be carried out on that one unit, but an inspection inside a unit should never be made unless it has definitely been determined to be faulty.

Equipment inspection is the step immediately after symptom analysis. Taking these two steps in turn the faulty area should be greatly reduced, and in many cases these two steps will isolate the fault. Neither of these steps should take very long and if they are carried out correctly they should almost invariably save large amounts of time in all fault-finding problems.

Turn to *Frame 90.*

90

To sum up on equipment inspection:

Equipment inspection uses all of our senses in an endeavour to pick out obvious faults. No tests should be carried out at this stage. A modified system of inspection is required on multi-unit equipment. This step, together with symptom analysis, should at least narrow the possible faulty area, if not determine the actual fault. With practice the operation of these two steps will become automatic but until this happens it is more efficient for you to think in clear logical steps, carrying out each move in the correct order.

Now turn to the next page for a review of this section.

Review of Equipment Inspection

The second step in logical fault finding should be to carry out EQUIP-MENT INSPECTION.

The purpose of equipment inspection is to find any immediately obvious faults.

All the senses should be used in this inspection, mainly looking for obvious faults, and occasionally finding faults by touch or smell.

No test equipment should be required.

The step should be very easily and quickly carried out.

In a multi-unit equipment, the inspection should be carried out first of all on the exteriors of the units and on the inter-unit connexions. Only when a faulty unit has been definitely isolated should equipment inspection be carried out inside a unit.

Now turn to the next page for the section test.

Test 2

Write down the answers to the following questions.

1. What is the name of the second step in logical fault finding?
2. Will this involve dismantling the equipment?
3. How long should it take to carry out this step?
4. Name three typical faults which you could expect to find in this step?
5. Which items of test gear will be required for this step?
6. How is this step applied to multi-unit equipment?
7. Under what circumstances should inspection be carried out inside a sub-unit?
8. What aids do you use when carrying out this step?

When you have written down the answers to these questions, turn to page *B* at the end of the book.

SIGNAL INJECTION & TRACING

You have now been taught the first two steps of logical fault finding: Symptom Analysis and Equipment Inspection. Neither of these steps required the use of test equipment, nor entailed dismantling equipment. However, carried out correctly they should enable a first estimate of the fault to be made and in many cases will enable the fault to be found. If the fault has not been found by this stage, then test equipment must be used as the fault is not an obvious one.

Assume that you are fault finding on a superhet receiver.

What would be the first type of test equipment to be used?

A. A multimeter *Frame 93*
B. A signal generator *Frame 95*
C. An oscilloscope *Frame 97*

92

Exactly the same rules hold good for the examples used earlier of the car and the ankle pain. In the case of the car whose engine would not start, consider that the symptom analysis and equipment inspection carried out have ascertained that the petrol supply is correct and the fault lies in there being no spark at the sparking plugs. Equipment inspection has shown that there are no obvious faults, and we now know that either there is no charge in the battery or there is a fault in the electrical circuit of the ignition.

If the fault was suspected to be that there was no charge in the battery then one simple check would be to connect up a battery which was known to contain sufficient charge. This would inject into the equipment a "signal" which was known to be correct, and the result could be monitored. We would, in fact, expect the engine to start. This test could be equated with signal injection in an electronic equipment.

Turn to *Frame 94*.

93

Your answer was that the first type of test equipment which you would use when fault finding on a superhet receiver was a multimeter.

There are a few particular examples where a multimeter would be useful as the first piece of test equipment. However, in normal circumstances, we should not yet concentrate on voltages at specific points and components. Rather we should attempt to isolate areas of the equipment as containing the fault or being correct. Consider what type of test equipment could isolate areas of the equipment as being faulty or correct.

Turn to *Frame 91* and try the question again.

94

If the fault in the car engine was suspected to be that there was no spark at the sparking plugs due to a fault in the ignition circuit, then the best test would be to attempt to trace the "signal" from the battery to determine the extent of the circuit in which it was correct, and the point in the circuit where it was not correct. This could easily be done by inducing a spark to jump from the h.t. lead or the plug to the chassis of the car. This test could be equated with signal tracing in an electronic equipment.

Turn to *Frame 96*.

Good. A signal generator would be the first piece of test equipment to be used. However, there will be some particular examples where a multimeter would be useful as the first test equipment and these cases will be dealt with later in the program. For normal purposes, the first test equipment which should be used is a signal generator.

An oscilloscope is a very useful aid to fault finding, but the wisdom of using it at this stage on a superhet receiver is in doubt. The oscilloscope will be more useful in more complicated equipments.

Whichever test equipment is used, whether the signal generator or the oscilloscope, the test is concerned with the signal in the equipment. The signal generator injects the necessary test signal and the output can be observed; the oscilloscope monitors whatever signal was present and this can be compared with the correct signal.

Using an oscilloscope is called SIGNAL TRACING.

Using a signal generator is called SIGNAL INJECTION.

One of these two steps should be the step immediately after symptom analysis and equipment inspection.

Turn to *Frame 92*.

96

Consider now the doctor attempting a diagnosis. After looking carefully at the fault, or the faulty area, he would then inject signals and monitor the output or trace signals which were already present. He could inject pressure signals by pressing at points around the area and monitoring the result this would have. This would further help to isolate the area of the fault, in the same way as in electronic equipments you should be constantly attempting to further isolate the area of the fault to progressively smaller areas. He could also trace signals which were already present by monitoring such things as pulse, blood pressure, temperature and respiration. The use of these would be determined by the fault and the area of the fault, that is in which particular piece of body equipment it occurred. In some cases he would find signal injection more convenient, and in some cases signal tracing would be more convenient, just as you will find them of differing importance according to the type of equipment you are working on and the actual type of fault on that equipment.

Turn to *Frame 98.*

97

Your answer was that the first type of test equipment which you would use when fault finding on a superhet receiver was an oscilloscope.

In some types of equipment the oscilloscope is a very useful aid to fault finding, but the wisdom of using it at this stage of fault finding on a superhet receiver is in doubt. The oscilloscope will be more useful in more complicated equipments.

Turn to *Frame 91* and try the question again.

c

98

So far we have seen that after symptom analysis and equipment inspection come signal tracing or signal injection; now to consider the use of these two tests in more detail with reference to electronic equipment.

Firstly, SIGNAL TRACING.

In an earlier example we considered a superhet receiver. Let us assume now that there is no sound output on any waveband, and the gain control has no effect. Symptom analysis and equipment inspection have been pursued as far as possible. Which of the following would be correct?

- A. Signal tracing should be carried out in the a.f. stages *Frame 100*
- B. Signal tracing should be carried out in the stages before the a.f. stages *Frame 102*
- C. Signal tracing should not be used in this case *Frame 104*

99

Now to consider SIGNAL INJECTION.

We saw that for signal tracing to be carried out successfully there must be a signal present in the equipment at some point. To carry out signal injection successfully, which of the following conditions would be required?

- A. A "normal" signal in all of the equipment *Frame 101*
- B. A "normal" signal in part of the equipment *Frame 103*
- C. No "normal" signal is required *Frame 105*

100

Carrying out signal tracing in the a.f. stages would not be the correct move.

You were told in the previous frame that there was no sound output on any waveband and therefore there must be no signal in the a.f. stages at some point. Moreover, you were told earlier in the program that signal tracing in a superhet receiver was not advisable. Therefore we should not use signal tracing in this example.

Turn to *Frame 104*.

101

If there was a normal signal in all of the equipment then we would hardly need to do any fault finding, and therefore signal injection would not be required.

You must think more carefully.

Turn to *Frame 99* and try the question again.

102

Carrying out signal tracing in the stages before the a.f. stages would not be the correct move. Although the fault may lie in this area you cannot be certain of isolating it with signal tracing. Moreover, earlier in the program you were told that signal tracing in a superhet receiver was not advisable. Therefore we should not use signal tracing in this example.

Turn to *Frame 104*.

103

You said that a "normal" signal was required in part of the equipment before signal injection could be carried out successfully.

In fact, a "normal" signal is not required anywhere in the equipment to enable signal injection to be carried out successfully. Whatever signal is required will be injected to the equipment.

Turn to *Frame 105*.

104

Correct. Signal tracing should not be used in this example.

Before you can carry out signal tracing you must be certain that there is a signal to trace! Once you have determined that there is no signal present then signal tracing is not going to give any advance, unless it is carried out in conjunction with signal injection.

However, there are many cases where signal tracing with an oscilloscope is extremely useful. In equipments where a specific waveform is required, or in circuits requiring pulse techniques, an oscilloscope is invaluable. However, in the simpler types of radio equipment it is not required. The particular uses of signal tracing do not require amplification here and they are not essential to the teaching of this fault-finding method.

Turn to *Frame 99*.

105

Correct. A "normal" signal is not required in any part of the equipment in order to carry out signal injection successfully. Whatever signal is required is injected and therefore signal injection can be performed regardless of the location of the fault.

Would you consider that signal injection can be used in any type of equipment?

A. Yes *Frame 107*
B. No *Frame 109*

106

The following frames will now consider in more detail the use of signal injection in electronic equipment. Remember that signal tracing is very similar, but will be dealt with at a later stage.

Whether signal tracing or signal injection is used, these must come *after* symptom analysis and equipment inspection. A flow chart is given at the back of this book which will summarize the use of these steps.

Turn to *Frame 108*.

107

Yes. Signal injection can be used in any type of equipment, provided that a signal generator is available which will provide the necessary type of signal.

In order to carry out signal injection successfully you will therefore require a good knowledge of the type of signal which should be present at each point in the equipment you are considering, and which type of signal generator will produce this signal.

It is impossible to overstress the importance of good theoretical knowledge of electronic equipment to efficient fault finding. This theoretical knowledge must include general electronic theory, particular knowledge of the equipment in question and the signal flow in it, and knowledge of test equipment and techniques.

Detailed knowledge of this type is not within the scope of this program, but it must be assumed that anyone attempting fault finding already has an adequate theoretical knowledge of the necessary electronic principles.

Turn to *Frame 106*.

108

Here is a more specific example on signal injection.

Consider an equipment consisting of eight stages, whose block diagram is as below.

Make a copy of this diagram as you will require it for several frames.

When you have done this, turn to *Frame 110*.

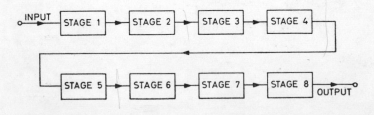

Your answer was that signal injection could not be used in all types of equipment. This is not correct.

Signal injection *can* be used in any equipment, the limiting factor being the availability of suitable signal generators.

Turn to *Frame 107*.

When a correct signal is fed into stage 1, there is no output from stage 8. Therefore one of the stages must be faulty.

Assume that symptom analysis and equipment inspection have been correctly performed, but the fault has not yet been isolated.

The next step will therefore be signal injection.

Where should the first test signal be injected?

A.	Between stages 7 and 8	*Frame 112*
B.	Between stages 1 and 2	*Frame 114*
C.	Between stages 4 and 5	*Frame 116*

Your answer was that your second test injection would be between stages 1 and 2. This is not correct.

When a test signal was injected between stages 4 and 5 it was found that the output was correct. Therefore stages 5, 6, 7 and 8 are correct and the fault must lie in one of the first four stages.

In the last test the correct move was to inject at the centre of the faulty area.

Try the question again.

Turn to *Frame 116*.

112

Your answer was that as the first step in signal injection, you would inject a test signal between stages 7 and 8. This is not correct.

If the faulty stage was stage 1, then six further tests like this would be needed to find the fault. You might be lucky and find that the faulty stage was stage 8 and that you only needed one test. However, the chances of this happening are small.

There is a better method of fault finding than the one you chose.

Have another attempt at the question.

Where should the first test signal be injected?

A. Between stages 4 and 5 *Frame 116*
B. Between stages 1 and 2 *Frame 120*

113

Correct. The second test signal should again be injected at the centre of the faulty area. The first test proved that the faulty area was the first four stages and therefore the second test signal should be injected at the centre of this area, i.e. between stages 2 and 3.

If the output from stage 8 is now correct, then all stages after stage 2 are correct, and the faulty area has been narrowed to either stage 1 or 2.

If the output from stage 8 is not now correct, then the fault must lie at some point after the input of stage 3. However, stages 5, 6, 7 and 8 were previously proved to be correct, and therefore the fault would now lie in either stage 3 or 4.

Wherever the fault lies, the faulty area has been narrowed to two stages after only two tests.

Now for the next step.

Assume that when the second test signal was injected between stages 2 and 3 there was no final output.

Where should the next test signal be injected?

  A. Between stages 1 and 2   *Frame 115*
  B. Between stages 2 and 3   *Frame 117*
  C. Between stages 3 and 4   *Frame 122*

114

Your answer was that as the first step in signal injection you would inject a test signal between stages 1 and 2. This is not correct.

Very little new information could be gained by this test. If the output was now normal then the faulty stage must be stage 1, but if the output was not normal then the faulty stage could be any of the other seven. The chance that the faulty stage is stage 1 is one in eight and therefore this is not a very efficient method of signal injection.

There is a better method of signal injection than the one you chose.

Have another attempt at the question.

Where should the first test signal be injected?

  A. Between stages 4 and 5   *Frame 116*
  B. Between stages 7 and 8   *Frame 120*

115

Your answer was that the third test signal should be injected between stages 1 and 2. This is not correct.

When the second test signal was injected between stages 2 and 3 there was no output from stage 8. Therefore the fault must lie in the last six stages. However, the last four stages were proved correct by the first test. Therefore the fault must now lie in stages 3 or 4. In this case there is no point in injecting a signal between stages 1 and 2 as these stages should be correct, and this test will give no new information.

Try the question again. Turn to *Frame 113*.

Correct. The first test signal should be injected between stages 4 and 5. Originally the fault could have been in any of the eight stages, and the correct injection point was in the centre of the faulty area.

If the output from stage 8 is now correct, then the fault must lie in the first four stages. If the output from stage 8 is not now correct, then the fault must lie in the last four stages.

Assume that the output from stage 8 was correct when a test signal was injected between stages 4 and 5.

Where should the next test signal be injected?

> *A.* Between stages 1 and 2   *Frame 111*
> *B.* Between stages 2 and 3   *Frame 113*
> *C.* Between stages 3 and 4   *Frame 119*
> *D.* Between stages 6 and 7   *Frame 121*

117

Your answer was that the third test signal should be injected between stages 2 and 3. This is not correct.

You cannot be concentrating. This test point was used for the second test signal. There is therefore no point in injecting the third test signal at this point.

The most important requirement of good fault finding is clear, logical thought, and you were not doing this when you gave your answer. If you cannot easily remember the steps you have taken, then you should make a note of them. In an actual fault-finding situation, you would be just as likely to mistake the actual steps taken as you were in this case.

Try the question again.

You may wish to recap on the problem. If so, turn to *Frame 110*.

If you wish to go directly to the question, turn to *Frame 113*.

118

Now draw out the eight stages again.

Make each stage the faulty stage in turn, and see how many test injections are required to find the fault, each time using the half-split method of signal injection.

Determine the maximum number of test injections required.

When you have done this, turn to *Frame 123*.

119

Your answer was that your second test injection would be between stages 3 and 4. This is not correct.

When a test signal was injected between stages 4 and 5 it was found that the output from stage 8 was correct. Therefore the last four stages are correct and the fault must lie in one of the first four stages.

In the last test the correct move was to inject at the centre of the faulty area.

Try the question again.

Turn to *Frame 116*.

120

You have twice given the incorrect answer to this question. The correct point of injection for the first test signal is not at either end of the chain of faulty stages, but is in the centre of the possible faulty area. This is very important and should be remembered and used later in the program.

Turn to *Frame 116*.

121

Your answer was that your second test injection would be between stages 6 and 7. This is not correct.

When a test signal was injected between stages 4 and 5 it was found that the output from stage 8 was correct. Therefore the last four stages were correct, and there is no point whatsoever in injecting between stages 6 and 7 as they lie in the last four stages.

In the last test the correct move was to inject at the centre of the faulty area.

Try the question again.

Turn to *Frame 116*.

122

Correct. The third test signal should now be injected between stages 3 and 4. The result of the second test proved that the fault lay in either stage 3 or 4, and we should again inject to the centre of the faulty area.

If the output from stage 8 is now correct, then stage 3 must be the faulty stage.

If the output from stage 8 is not now correct, then stage 4 must be the faulty stage.

The faulty stage has therefore been isolated after carrying out only three test injections.

Each test consisted of injecting a test signal to the *centre* of the possible faulty area, determining whether the fault lay in the first half or the second half. This is called the HALF-SPLIT method of signal injection and you should always follow this method.

Turn to *Frame 118*.

You should have noted that no matter which stage you chose as containing the fault, three is the maximum number of steps needed to find the fault, using the half-split method.

Another popular method is to start at the end of the chain and progress one stage at a time until the faulty stage is isolated. Using this method the fault might be found with less than three steps, but this would only occur if the fault were in stage 7 or 8. Any other stage would require three or more steps to isolate.

Therefore the half-split method is much superior and should always be used. Very occasionally it will not be the quickest, but on average it will save large amounts of time. This will make your fault finding more efficient.

Now to try this method with a typical superhet receiver.

Turn to *Frame 124.*

Now to look at this half-split method in a more usual circuit.

The block diagram below represents a typical superhet receiver. Make a copy of this diagram as you will need it for several frames. When you have done this, turn to *Frame 125.*

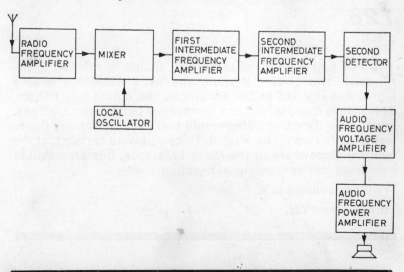

Half-splitting this equipment can be seen to present more of a problem than the previous example. The superhet has no immediately apparent mid-point. There are, however, eight stages and therefore the mid-point should be between the two i.f. amplifiers. Even so, in this special case it is best not to inject at this point since it is in the middle of the i.f. stages. In the case of the superhet it will be better to split the stages into the r.f. stages, the i.f. stages and the a.f. stages. Each section can then be dealt with in turn.

This is not exact half-splitting, but it shows how the rules of fault finding have to be adapted to suit particular equipments. Straightforward half-splitting can only be used very occasionally.

Let us suppose that this superhet receiver has a fault of a type called "catastrophic", i.e. there is a complete breakdown of the output signal. Both symptom analysis and equipment inspection have been pursued as far as possible and the fault has not yet been isolated. Signal injection should be the next step.

Where should the first test signal be injected?

A. To the r.f. amplifier *Frame 127*
B. Between the first and second i.f. amplifiers *Frame 129*
C. Between the second detector and the second i.f. amplifier *Frame 131*

You said that the second test signal should be injected to the r.f. amplifier. However, the previous test showed that when a signal was injected to the a.f. stages, the output was correct. This means that the fault lies somewhere before the a.f. stages. Injecting to the r.f. amplifier would only confirm this and therefore this step would be wasted. Once you were certain that the fault lay somewhere in the r.f. or i.f. stages, this area should have been half-split by signal injection.

Try the question again.

Turn to *Frame 131*.

Your answer was that you would inject the first test signal to the r.f. amplifier. This is not correct.

As you would be injecting to the beginning of the receiver you would get no output from the loudspeaker, as we already know that there is a fault in the receiver somewhere. Therefore this test would give no new information concerning the fault and it would be wasting time and effort.

Signal injection should progressively narrow down the faulty area, and you were taught in the previous example that the most efficient way of doing this was by using the half-split method.

Try the question again, and remember to use half-splitting.

Turn to *Frame 125*.

Your answer was that the second test signal should be injected to the point between the mixer and the first i.f. amplifier. Good.

When the first test signal was injected it proved that the a.f. stages were correct. Therefore the fault lay somewhere before these stages. In this case half-splitting can be carried out, and the mid-point of the faulty area is the point between the mixer and the first i.f. amplifier.

This point is also correct if you remembered the maxim that the receiver should be split up into three sections, the r.f. section, the i.f. section and the a.f. section. As the a.f. section has been proved to be correct, the next test signal should be injected to split the r.f. and i.f. sections.

Care is needed to see that the correct test signal is injected. In this case the correct test signal would be the i.f. frequency, amplitude-modulated with an audio frequency, usually 1 kHz.

If you injected this test signal, what would be the best method of checking the output?

A. By monitoring output with an oscilloscope   *Frame 130*
B. By listening at the loudspeaker   *Frame 132*
C. By using an output meter   *Frame 134*

129

Your answer was that you would inject the first test signal between the first and the second i.f. amplifiers.

This is, in fact, the centre of the chain of stages, so you would be correct in this. However, you were also told in the previous frame that it was more efficient to split the receiver into sections, the r.f. section, the i.f. section and the a.f. section rather than to carry out exact half-splitting.

In this case, it would be better to inject a test signal to the point between the second detector and the second i.f. amplifier to isolate the fault to the a.f. stages or to before this point.

Turn to *Frame 131*.

130

Monitoring the output of the receiver with an oscilloscope would be one way of checking the output, but a check of this extent is not required at this stage. For the purpose of the test in progress, it will be sufficient to listen at the loudspeaker to check the output.

Turn to *Frame 132*.

131

Your answer was that the first test signal should be injected between the second detector and the first a.f. amplifier. This is correct.

You will remember that we said that this equipment could not be exactly half-split as this was inconvenient, and it should be split into three sections, the r.f. stages, the i.f. stages and the a.f. stages. Of these three the first section to test is the a.f.

When this test signal is injected, the output is normal.

Where should the next test signal be injected?

   A. To the r.f. amplifier   *Frame 126*
   B. Between the mixer and the first i.f. amplifier   *Frame 128*
   C. Between the first and second a.f. amplifiers   *Frame 133*

In fact all three methods of checking the output are correct, but for the purposes of this test listening at the loudspeaker would provide a sufficient test of whether or not the injected signal was producing a satisfactory output.

Remember that unnecessary complications are a complete waste of time.

The audio frequency most used for test purposes is 1 kHz and you should make yourself familiar with this frequency so that you can easily recognize it when you hear it. You should also be able to distinguish 50 Hz and 100 Hz hum in the loudspeaker produced by the rectifier stages.

Now to recap on the problem. The last test was to inject a test signal to the first i.f. amplifier. If the output is now correct, then the fault must lie in the r.f. stages. If the output is not correct, then the fault must lie in the i.f. stages.

Let us assume that the output is correct, and that the r.f. stages are therefore at fault.

Where should the next test signal be injected?

A. At the control grid of the mixer valve   *Frame 135*
B. At the injector grid of the mixer valve   *Frame 138*
C. At the control grid of the r.f. amplifier   *Frame 141*

You said that the next test signal should be injected between the first and second a.f. amplifiers.

The main requirement of efficient fault finding is clear, logical thought and this was missing in your answer.

The previous test proved that the a.f. stages were correct since a test signal injected to the first a.f. stage produced a normal output. Injecting to the second a.f. amplifier is re-testing a stage which has already been tested and found to be correct.

The faulty area must be before the a.f. stages, and this is where the next test should take place.

Attempt the question again.   Turn to *Frame 131*.

134

Checking the output of the receiver by the use of an output meter would be a good way of carrying out this test, but at this stage is unnecessarily complicated. For the purpose of the test in progress, it will be sufficient to listen at the loudspeaker to check the output.

Turn to *Frame 132*.

135

Right. When the r.f. stages have been found to contain the fault, they should be split by signal injection. The obvious place is to inject to the mixer valve. However, there are two possible places to inject a signal, the control grid and the injector grid.

To inject a test signal at the injector grid would require a signal from the r.f. amplifier to be correct, to mix with the simulated local oscillator signal and produce the correct intermediate frequency. If you injected at the injector grid and did not have the correct output then the fault has still not been isolated, and could be in either the r.f. stages or the mixer.

Injecting a test signal at the control grid of the mixer would involve the same difficulties, requiring the correct signal from the local oscillator to produce an output signal, unless the signal injected to the control grid of the mixer were the intermediate frequency. This would test the mixer stage by itself, without requiring other signals, and would prove to be very useful.

Assume that when the intermediate frequency is injected to the control grid of the mixer valve, there is no output from the loudspeaker.

Where should the next test signal be injected?

- A. At the injector grid of the mixer valve   *Frame 137*
- B. At the anode of the mixer valve   *Frame 139*
- C. At the control grid of the r.f. amplifier valve   *Frame 142*

You should see that the principle of half-splitting the faulty areas by signal injection is a very useful aid in fault finding. It can be applied to any type of equipment, and can be pursued to sub-stage level.

In almost every practical example, you will not be able to perform exact half-splitting, but you should keep to this method as closely as possible.

Even though the method of half-splitting by signal injection may have to be modified slightly, it will almost invariably save time and effort, and will thus make your fault finding more efficient. At all stages it is essential that you use clear, logical thought, progressively narrowing down the possible faulty area until the actual fault is found.

If the equipment is contained in several units, then it is important to work first of all in units, to determine which is the faulty unit.

A summary of this method is contained in the flow sheet at the end of the program.

Turn to *Frame 140*.

When there was no output from the loudspeaker on injecting the intermediate frequency to the control grid of the mixer valve, you wished to inject the next test signal at the injector grid of the mixer valve.

This would not be correct as the previous test had proved that it was the mixer stage itself which was at fault, since the intermediate frequency injected to the control grid gave no output. Therefore no new information concerning the fault could be obtained from this test.

Try the question again.

Turn to *Frame 135*.

138

When the fault had been isolated to the r.f. stages, you wished to inject a test signal to the injector grid of the mixer valve. This is not a good move.

This signal would have to be the simulated local oscillator signal and the r.f. stages would have to be tuned to this signal, in order to produce the correct intermediate frequency on mixing with the r.f. signal. However, the r.f. signal is not known to be correct. Therefore even when the r.f. stages are correctly tuned to this signal, the fact that there is no output from the receiver has not isolated the fault very much further.

Try the question again.

Turn to *Frame 132*.

139

Your answer was that the next test signal should be injected at the anode of the mixer valve. This is correct.

The previous test had proved that the mixer stage was at fault. Half-splitting can be continued to split a single stage, and in this case it would be an advantage.

This test would prove whether the fault lay before or after the anode of the mixer stage, and in fact could also be used to advantage in other stages.

When injecting test signals in this way, there is one precaution which you should especially observe. The test point for your injection carries h.t. potential and if the oscillator you are using does not have a blocking capacitor in the output, then the h.t. could damage the oscillator. If you are not certain whether your oscillator contains this blocking capacitor, you should insert one in the output lead.

Signal injection can be carried further than this and could in fact be pursued to component level, but this would not prove an advantage in this method. Do not pursue signal injection beyond splitting a stage.

Turn to *Frame 136*.

You saw earlier that there was a part of the superhet receiver where signal injection was very difficult. This was the mixer and local oscillator section.

A circuit of this type is called a convergent circuit. More than one input must be correct before the output is correct. In fact, usually all of the inputs to a convergent circuit must be correct before the correct output can be obtained.

An example of a convergent circuit is shown below.

Make a copy of this diagram as you will require it for several frames.

Turn to *Frame 143*.

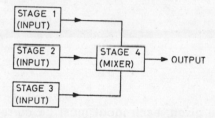

When the fault has already been isolated to the r.f. stages, injecting a test signal to the control grid of the r.f. amplifier is not going to yield any new information concerning the fault. You must think clearly and logically. If you cannot remember which steps have been taken then make a list of them as you do them.

Turn to *Frame 142*.

142

When there was no output from the loudspeaker on injecting the intermediate frequency to the control grid of the mixer valve, you wished to inject the next test signal at the control grid of the r.f. amplifier valve. This is not correct.

The fault has been proved to be in the mixer stage and not in the r.f. amplifier stage by the previous test. You are not thinking very clearly.

Be honest with yourself, and if you consider that you have not grasped the method of half-splitting, then turn to *Frame 124*.

If this was just a simple mistake, then try the question again, being very careful to think logically of the previous tests. Turn to *Frame 132*.

143

In the example given, each input must be correct to give the correct output. If any of the three inputs is not correct then there will either be no output at all or an incorrect output, depending upon the exact type of equipment.

There is no need at this stage to state that a specific equipment is being used because this course teaches a basic method of fault finding which can be applied to any electronic equipment.

Let us suppose that there is not the correct output from this convergent circuit. What should be your first step, assuming that symptom analysis and equipment inspection have not isolated the fault?

A. Check the circuit of stage 4   *Frame 145*
B. Inject inputs 1, 2 and 3 in turn to stage 4   *Frame 147*
C. Check the circuit of stages 1, 2 and 3 by signal injection
    Frame 149

The general rules for CONVERGENT CIRCUITS are then:

Replace each input stage in turn by a simulated signal.

If the correct output is obtained when a certain input stage is replaced by a substitute signal, then this is the faulty stage.

If the correct output is not obtained on any of the simulated inputs, then the output stage contains the fault.

Turn to *Frame 146*.

145

Your answer was that the first step would be to check stage 4. This stage might in fact contain the fault, but you should not begin checking the circuit of stage 4 unless you are certain that the fault does lie in this stage.

Signal injection test should be completed before circuit checking is commenced.

Try the question again.   Turn to *Frame 143*.

146

For an example on convergent circuits, we will use the mixer section of a superhet receiver.

The following diagram represents the block diagram of a simplified section of a superhet receiver. Make a copy of this diagram as you will need it for several frames.

When you have done this, turn to *Frame 148*.

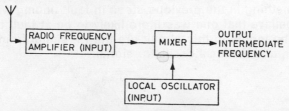

147

Your answer was that inputs 1, 2 and 3 should each be injected in turn to stage 4. This is correct.

Suppose that stage 2 is at fault. Stages 1 and 3 will still be giving the correct inputs for stage 4. Therefore when a substitute signal replaces the non-existent signal from stage 2, all three inputs to stage 4 will be correct, and the correct output from stage 4 will be obtained.

The same argument will hold good for either stage 1 or stage 3 being the faulty stage.

Now suppose that stage 4 is at fault. This would not be obvious at first. However, if the three inputs from stages 1, 2 and 3 were each simulated in turn by signal injection, and there was still no output from stage 4, then the fault must be in stage 4. If the fault had been in any of the three other stages, the correct output from stage 4 would have been obtained for one of the three inputs.

Turn to *Frame 144*.

148

Now we can have another look at the earlier example we dealt with, namely the local oscillator and mixer sections of the superhet receiver. This is an example of a convergent circuit. We found a particular way of dealing with this circuit by injecting the intermediate frequency to the control grid of the mixer valve. This would show whether the local oscillator or the mixer were at fault.

However, we can also deal with this circuit following the rules we have just established. This entails replacing each input stage in turn by a simulated signal. There is no particular preference for taking one input before the other unless there was something in the previous steps in fault finding which led you to believe that one was more likely to be at fault than the other. The inputs in this circuit are the r.f. signal from the r.f. amplifier, and the local oscillator signal.

In this circuit, when the test signals are injected, care must be taken to ensure that the stages are correctly tuned, or else the input signal must be varied to fit the tuning of the stages.

If the correct output is obtained when the r.f. signal is simulated, then the r.f. amplifier is the faulty stage.

If the correct output is obtained when the local oscillator signal is simulated, then the fault lies in this stage.

If the output is not correct when either of the simulated signals is injected, then the fault lies in the mixer stage.

Turn to *Frame 150.*

149

Your answer was that the first step you would carry out would be to check the circuits of the individual stages 1, 2 and 3. This is not correct.

You cannot be certain that the fault lies in any of these stages, it could lie in stage 4. If this were the case, then checking the individual circuits of stages 1, 2 and 3 could be a very lengthy and wasteful test.

Signal injection should be completed before circuit checking is commenced.

Try the question again.

Turn to *Frame 143.*

150

Convergent circuits can also be dealt with by the use of signal tracing.

We can use the same general block diagram as before. You should have a copy of this diagram, but if not here it is again. Make a copy of it.

When you have done this, turn to *Frame 152*.

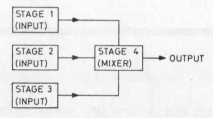

151

This section of the superhet receiver could also be checked fairly easily by the use of signal tracing. An oscilloscope could be used to check that the r.f. amplifier is giving the correct output, and that the local oscillator is giving the correct output. If either of these were not correct, then this would be found from the trace on the screen. If both of these signals were correct, but there was still not the correct output from the mixer stage, then the mixer stage is at fault.

There are therefore a selection of methods which could be used on a convergent circuit. Each will have certain advantages on specific circuits, and it will be up to you to ensure that you always use the most efficient.

Turn to *Frame 153*.

152

Consider that we have the same fault as before: there is no output from stage 4.

If you had the correct test equipment available, each of the outputs of stage 1, 2 and 3 could be monitored. If any of these are found to be incorrect, then the appropriate stage is obviously the faulty stage. If all three of these signals are found to be correct, then the faulty stage is stage 4.

This method is more straightforward than signal injection, but the necessary test equipment is not always available.

Turn to *Frame 154*.

153

A type of circuit opposite to a convergent circuit can some-times be found. A circuit in which one stage gives more than one output is a DIVERGENT CIRCUIT. An example of a diver-gent circuit is given below.

Make a copy of this diagram as you will require it for several frames.

Turn to *Frame 155*.

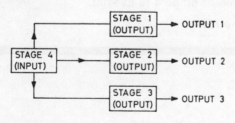

154

For an example on signal tracing, we can use the mixer section of a superhet receiver, as we did before. You should already have the diagram for this section, but if not you can copy it again from the diagram below.

When you have done this, turn to *Frame 151*.

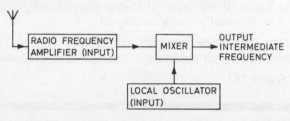

155

In this type of circuit any one of the output stages 1, 2 or 3 could be faulty and the other two outputs would still be correct. For this type of circuit, signal tracing is more convenient than signal injection. Each output should be checked in turn by monitoring the output. If any of the outputs is not correct, then this is where the fault lies. If all of the outputs are incorrect, then the whole of stage 4 is at fault.

Turn to *Frame 156*.

156

If no monitoring equipment were available, then the test would have to be carried out by signal injection.

In this case, a simulated output of stage 4 should be injected to each of stages 1, 2 and 3 in turn. If the output of stage 1 is correct when the simulated signal is injected to it, then this stage must be correct. If the output of stage 1 is incorrect when the simulated signal is injected to it, then this stage is not correct. Similarly for the two other output stages.

However, if all three outputs are correct when the simulated signals are injected to them, then the stage at fault must be stage 4.

Turn to *Frame 157*.

157

An example of a divergent stage is sometimes found in a.m. receivers, where the second detector and the a.g.c. are contained in the same stage. In this case either one of these outputs could be correct or incorrect, independent of the other output. The procedures outlined in the previous frames would have to be adhered to.

As in convergent circuits, there are several methods which can be applied. With experience you will be able to choose the most efficient.

The possibility of incorrect connexions between stages has been ignored in this consideration in order to simplify the treatment.

Now turn to the next page for a review of this section.

Review of Signal Injection and Signal Tracing

The third step in logical fault finding should be to carry out **SIGNAL INJECTION** or **SIGNAL TRACING**.

The purpose of signal injection (and signal tracing) is to isolate a single stage as containing the fault.

Signal injection is based on the half-split method. This enables the faulty stage to be isolated in the smallest number of tests. The signal is always injected as near as possible to the mid-point of the faulty area.

The test equipment required is basically a signal generator with an output meter or oscilloscope an optional extra.

Signal injection is generally preferable to signal tracing as the signal generator should always supply the correct signal, and during signal tracing it is not always certain that the correct signal is in fact present.

In a multi-unit equipment, do not split a sub-unit until the sub-unit has been proved to be faulty. Confine signal injection to the input points of units for the first test.

Convergent and divergent circuits require special treatment dependent upon the actual circuit configuration.

Now continue with the section test below.

Test 3

Write down the answers to the following questions.

1. What is the name of the third step in logical fault finding?
2. What is the purpose of this step?
3. What test equipment would be required?

   State the correct input point for signals to be injected in the following cases:

4.
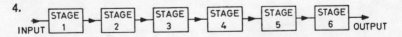

   There is no output from stage 6 when the correct input is injected to stage 1.

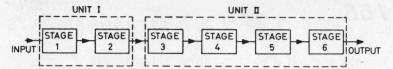

INPUT

UNIT I

STAGE 1 → STAGE 2

UNIT II

STAGE 3 → STAGE 4 → STAGE 5 → STAGE 6

OUTPUT

No output from stage 6 when correct input is injected to stage 1.

6.

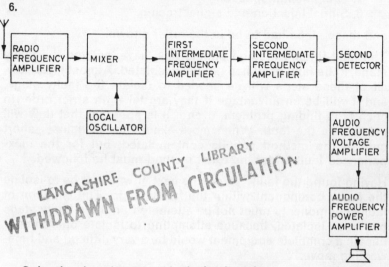

RADIO FREQUENCY AMPLIFIER → MIXER → FIRST INTERMEDIATE FREQUENCY AMPLIFIER → SECOND INTERMEDIATE FREQUENCY AMPLIFIER → SECOND DETECTOR

LOCAL OSCILLATOR

AUDIO FREQUENCY VOLTAGE AMPLIFIER

AUDIO FREQUENCY POWER AMPLIFIER

Only a low hum is present in the loudspeaker.

7.

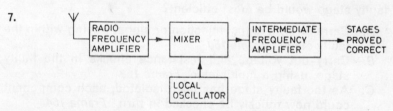

RADIO FREQUENCY AMPLIFIER → MIXER → INTERMEDIATE FREQUENCY AMPLIFIER → STAGES PROVED CORRECT

LOCAL OSCILLATOR

No output from the i.f. stage when correct signal is injected to the r.f. stage.

8.

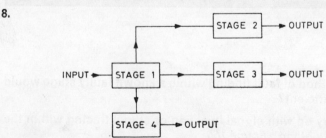

INPUT → STAGE 1

STAGE 2 → OUTPUT

STAGE 3 → OUTPUT

STAGE 4 → OUTPUT

No output from stage 4 when correct signal is injected to stage 1.

When you have written down the answers to these questions, turn to page *C* at the end of the book.

158

The steps which have been carried out so far are

1. Symptom analysis
2. Equipment inspection
3. Signal injection and signal tracing

and these steps had to be in the order shown.

The fault-finding method should now have isolated the faulty stage, if the fault itself had not been isolated. Almost invariably, all of these steps will be needed to isolate the faulty stage, and it will be an advantage if they are taken in strict order in each fault-finding problem, even if it is apparent that they will not isolate the fault. When more experience is gained, short cuts in the method can be contemplated, but for the inexperienced fault finder the exact method must be followed.

Having found the faulty stage, the next move must be to isolate the faulty component within the faulty stage. The isolation of faulty components must not be attempted until the faulty stage has been isolated, because attempting to isolate one component in a complete equipment would be a very difficult and time-wasting move.

Which method of finding the faulty component within a known faulty stage would be most efficient?

A. Carry on with signal injection or signal tracing within the faulty stage   *Frame 160*
B. Carry out voltage and resistance checks in the faulty stage, using a multimeter   *Frame 162*
C. As the faulty stage has been isolated, each component could now quickly be checked in turn   *Frame 164*

159

Which method of fault finding within a known faulty stage would be most efficient?

A. Carry on with signal injection or signal tracing within the faulty stage   *Frame 166*
B. Carry out voltage and resistance checks in the faulty stage, using a multimeter   *Frame 162*

160

Your answer was that the faulty component within a faulty stage could most efficiently be found by carrying on with signal injection and signal tracing. This is not correct.

Although it is sometimes convenient to half-split a faulty stage by the use of signal injection or signal tracing, the method ceases to be efficient after this level, and other methods become more efficient.

Try the question again.

Turn to *Frame 158*.

161

Suppose that in the superhet receiver which was used earlier a test signal was injected to the control grid of the audio frequency voltage amplifier and no output was observed at the loudspeaker. When a test signal was injected to the control grid of the audio frequency power amplifier, the output was normal. Therefore the fault lies in the audio frequency voltage amplifier.

The circuit for this stage is shown below. Make a copy of this circuit as you will require it for several frames.

When you have done this, turn to *Frame 163*.

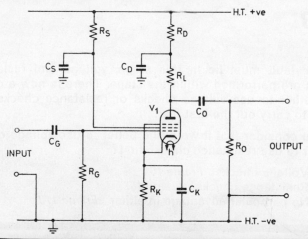

162

The most efficient method of isolating a faulty component within a faulty stage is to use VOLTAGE AND RESISTANCE CHECKS within the stage. This is then the fourth step in the fault-finding method.

In general, the only item of test equipment required for this step is a multimeter, but you must also be supplied with details of the voltages present at test points and with sufficient information to determine the resistance between two points in the circuit.

Once this information has been supplied, then voltage and resistance checks are very easy to perform. Unfortunately, they are so easy to perform that there is a general tendency in all fault finding to use this method excessively. Remember that this method should not be used until the previous steps of symptom analysis, equipment inspection, and signal injection or signal tracing have been completed. In certain cases an experienced fault finder would be able to omit one or more of these steps because of his experience. In fact he would then be performing symptom analysis to such a degree that the fault had been found, or suspected. Do not attempt to do this until you have sufficient experience. Above all, think logically and clearly.

For an example on voltage and resistance checks, turn to *Frame 161*.

163

As the fault must lie in this stage, voltage and resistance checks are performed within the stage. There is now a choice of whether to use voltage checks or resistance checks, and where to carry out the first test.

Do you consider that it would be better to use voltage checks first, or to use resistance checks first?

A. Voltage checks   *Frame 165*
B. Resistance checks   *Frame 167*
C. No particular advantage in either   *Frame 170*

164

Your answer was that the faulty component within a faulty stage could most efficiently be found by checking each component in turn. This is not correct.

Although the fault has been isolated to one stage, there could still be a very large number of components within this stage. To check each component in turn would take a long time and would not be efficient. In some cases, the fault might be found very quickly by chance, but in other cases the fault might be the last component to be tested.

NEVER carry out random testing of a component, unless you have definite grounds for considering that the fault is most likely to be that component.

Have another attempt at the question.

Turn to *Frame 159*.

165

In practice it will usually be more efficient to perform voltage checks before resistance checks.

Voltage measurements will be taken with the equipment switched on, but usually with no signal input. The majority of voltage measurements made will be d.c. measurements, such as the anode voltage or other electrode voltages, h.t. voltage, etc., but occasionally a.c. measurements will be made.

In the example amplifier you were given, which a.c. voltage measurement would be useful?

    A. Input signal voltage   *Frame 168*
    B. Output signal voltage   *Frame 171*
    C. Valve heater voltage   *Frame 173*

166

Your answer was that the faulty component within a faulty stage could most efficiently be found by carrying on with signal injection and signal tracing. This is not correct.

Although it is sometimes convenient to half-split a faulty stage by the use of signal injection or signal tracing, the method ceases to be efficient after this level, and other methods become more efficient.

Turn to *Frame 162*.

167

Your answer was that resistance checks should be the first test carried out on a faulty stage. These will help to isolate the faulty component in the faulty stage, but it will be found more efficient to use voltage checks before resistance checks.

Turn to *Frame 165*.

168

The input signal voltage would not be a usual voltage measurement taken during voltage and resistance checks.

You were not thinking very clearly when you gave this answer.

Turn to *Frame 175*.

169

Your answer was that the anode voltage would be the most useful measurement. This would be useful, but there would not be much difference in this circuit between the usefulness of the cathode voltage measurement and the anode voltage measurement.

Turn to *Frame 176*.

170

Your answer was that there would be no particular advantage in either of the steps of voltage or resistance checks as the first step in isolating the faulty component in a faulty stage.

In fact, voltage checks will be found to be more efficient if they are carried out before resistance checks.

Turn to *Frame 165*.

171

The output signal voltage would not be a usual voltage measurement taken during voltage and resistance checks.

You were not thinking very clearly when you gave this answer.

Turn to *Frame 175*.

172

You said that because the cathode voltage was correct, then all of the stage must be correct. This is not so.

There are faults which could occur in the circuit which would leave the cathode potential correct but which would mean that there was a fault in the stage. In any case you were told that this stage was faulty, therefore it could not be correct to say that there was not a fault in the stage.

This test should only prove that a certain part of the circuit is correct. Our tests are designed to gradually diminish the possible faulty area, and that is what should result from this test.

Consider the circuit very carefully and make an estimate of which parts of the circuit are definitely proved to be correct by the result of this test.

Attempt the question again.

If the cathode voltage is correct, what can you say about the circuit?

  A. The section of the circuit, R_D, R_L, V_1, R_K and C_K is correct
     Frame 174
  B. Only R_K and C_K are correct   *Frame 179*

173

Signal voltages are not normally measured on a multimeter, and you were told earlier that this was the only necessary item of test equipment in voltage and resistance checks.

Moreover, you were told that there was usually no signal input to the equipment when these tests were being performed.

There are certain specialized exceptions to this rule, but they will not concern us here.

However, there is an a.c. voltage measurement which can be taken in a circuit such as the example you were given of an audio frequency amplifier, or in fact in any valve circuit. This is, of course, the valve heater voltage. In British equipment this voltage is usually 6·3 volts a.c. Even so, this voltage does not always have to be taken to ensure that the heater is working correctly, as you will see later.

An example of other a.c. measurements required in certain cases is the testing of the transformer winding voltages in a rectifier circuit.

Now we know that when we have a faulty stage such as the example you were given, the first check on the stage will be to carry out d.c. voltage measurements.

Which d.c. voltage measurement should be the most useful?

A. The anode voltage   *Frame 169*
B. The cathode voltage   *Frame 176*
C. The control grid voltage   *Frame 178*

174

Correct. If the cathode voltage is correct, then it is almost certain that the section of the circuit from R_D down to R_K and C_K is correct. This proves that the valve is conducting correctly, and therefore there is no need to individually check these components or the valve heater. The fault in the circuit would then have to be in one of the other components, in the coupling circuits, or the screen grid circuit.

Suppose that you measured the anode voltage instead of the cathode voltage, and this was found to be zero. What would you now say about the circuit?

A. There is a short circuit between the anode and h.t.
   Frame 177
B. There is an open circuit between the anode and h.t.
   Frame 180
C. There is a short circuit between the anode and earth
   Frame 182
D. There is an open circuit between the anode and earth
   Frame 184

175

You were told that signals were not injected to the equipment whilst voltage and resistance checks were being taken.

Moreover, multimeters will not normally be used for measuring signal voltages, and you were told that only a multimeter was necessary for this stage of fault finding.

Turn to *Frame 173*.

176

In the circuit we are using, there will not be much difference in the advantage of measuring the anode voltage or the cathode voltage. Either voltage would tell us whether the valve was conducting correctly.

However, in circuits where the valve has an inductive load rather than a resistive load, cathode voltages will be more useful. This is due to the fact that the voltage drop across an inductive load is usually very small, and no significant difference would be noted in the anode voltage when the valve was conducting and when it was not conducting.

Unfortunately, some circuits with an inductive load also have the cathode at earth potential, and in this case the cathode voltage would not be a valid measurement.

In the circuit of the audio frequency voltage amplifier which we are using as an example, either the cathode voltage or the anode voltage could be taken as the first voltage measurement. Let us look a little more closely at these measurements.

If the cathode voltage is correct, what can you say about the circuit?

A. All of the amplifier circuit is correct *Frame 172*
B. The section of the circuit, R_D, R_L, V_1, R_K, and C_K, is correct *Frame 174*
C. Only R_K and C_K are correct *Frame 179*

177

No. If there were a short circuit between the anode and h.t. then the anode voltage would be equal to h.t. voltage.

Make another attempt at the question.

Turn to *Frame 174*.

178

Your answer was that the most useful voltage would be the control grid voltage. This is not correct. There is another voltage which will be more useful.

Make another attempt at the question.

Turn to *Frame 173*.

179

As the cathode voltage was correct, you said that only R_K and C_K would be correct.

If the voltage at the cathode is to have the correct value, then the current through the cathode resistor, and therefore through the valve, must also be correct. If the current through the valve is correct, then all of the circuit through the valve from h.t. to earth must be correct, i.e. R_D, R_L, V_1, R_K and C_K must all be correct.

Turn to *Frame 174*.

180

Your answer was that, when the anode voltage was zero, there must be an open circuit between the anode and h.t. This is one possible solution, but the fault could also be a short circuit between the anode and earth. Either of these faults could produce an anode voltage of zero. However, the short circuit from anode to earth is likely to be found by inspection because it would be produced by such faults as a piece of solder shorting out on the valve base, or a broken lead on R_L or C_O shorting out to chassis. These would be found by carrying out an equipment inspection of the faulty stage.

The open circuit between the anode and h.t. could be a broken lead, but could also be produced by the breakdown of components. The actual fault would be isolated by a more detailed examination and testing of the relevant portion of the circuit.

Now suppose that the measured anode voltage is the same as the h.t. voltage. What could you now say about the circuit?

A. There is a short circuit between the anode and h.t.
   Frame 183
B. There is an open circuit between the anode and h.t.
   Frame 185
C. There is a short circuit between the anode and earth
   Frame 187
D. There is an open circuit between the anode and earth
   Frame 189

181

You said that you would check each component between h.t. and earth. This would find the faulty component sooner or later but it is not an efficient method. We should not find it necessary to check each individual component. If the method of fault finding is carried out correctly, only one component needs to be checked since our tests will isolate the one faulty component.

Never check each component. This will almost invariably take more time than following the method correctly.

Try the question again.

Turn to *Frame 191*.

182

Your answer was that there would be a short circuit between the anode and earth. This would give the reading of zero volts on the anode, but this would more likely be due to an open circuit between the anode and h.t.

Turn to *Frame 180*.

183

Your answer was that there would be a short circuit between the anode and h.t. This is correct.

However, the fault could also bo an open circuit between the anode and earth.

Turn to *Frame 191*.

184

No. If there were an open circuit between the anode and earth then there would be no current through the resistors R_D and R_L. Therefore the resistance would have no effect upon the potential difference between the anode and h.t., and the anode would then be at h.t. potential.

Make another attempt at the question.

Turn to *Frame 174*.

185

No. If there were an open circuit between the anode and h.t. then the anode potential would be zero.

Make another attempt at the question.

Turn to *Frame 180*.

186

Correct. The anode voltage and the cathode voltage considered together will show exactly where the fault lies. Measuring the resistance between the cathode and earth will also give sufficient information. However, while you are measuring one voltage, it is easier to go on with more voltage measurements before going to resistance checks.

Once the fault has definitely been established to be either a short circuit between the anode and h.t. or an open circuit between the anode and earth, the faulty area has been narrowed down to a very small area. Further checks will then isolate the faulty component.

Now suppose that you wanted to check the control grid bias in the amplifier circuit you were given as the example. How would you carry out this test?

A. Measure the d.c. voltage between the control grid and earth   *Frame 188*
B. Measure the a.c. voltage between the control grid and earth   *Frame 190*
C. Measure the d.c. voltage between the cathode and earth *Frame 192*

187

No. If there were a short circuit between the anode and earth then the anode potential would be zero.

Make another attempt at the question.

Turn to *Frame 180*.

188

If you attempted to measure the d.c. potential between the control grid and earth you would probably be disappointed. The voltage drop across the grid resistor is very small and is due to the grid leakage current. It is not the grid bias potential.

It is assumed throughout this program that you have an adequate knowledge of simple electronic theory, and you should not have made this mistake.

Turn to *Frame 186* and try the question again.

189

Your answer was that there would be an open circuit between the anode and earth. This is correct.

However, the fault could also be a short circuit between the anode and h.t.

Turn to *Frame 191*.

190

The a.c. voltage between the control grid and earth is the signal input to the stage. This could probably not be measured with your meter, but in fact this voltage would not be present as you were told that voltage checks were on static voltages, i.e. there was no signal present. Attempting to do this would be a complete waste of time.

You must think clearly and logically at all times.

Turn to *Frame 186* and try the question again.

191

Right. The fault could be either a short circuit between the anode and h.t., or an open circuit between the anode and earth. The test made could not differentiate between these two possibilities.

How could you tell whether the fault was a short circuit or an open circuit?

A. Check each component between h.t. and earth *Frame 181*
B. Measure the cathode voltage *Frame 186*
C. Measure the resistance between the cathode and earth *Frame 193*

192

To measure the control grid to earth static voltage you should measure the cathode to earth static voltage. The grid bias is the voltage of the control grid with respect to the cathode. This circuit had auto-cathode bias, and the bias voltage is produced across R_K by the action of the valve current. Measuring the d.c. voltage between the control grid and earth would at most give a reading of the leakage current. The a.c. voltage from the control grid to earth is the signal input voltage to the stage, and in this case the reading should be zero as you were told that all voltage readings are normally taken without signals.

One more point about voltage readings. You should normally be told of the tolerance of the voltages at the test points. Suppose that a certain test point has a specified voltage of 175 volts, and the tolerance is 10%. Would a voltage of 190 volts at this test point be acceptable?

A. Yes *Frame 194*
B. No *Frame 196*

Measuring the resistance between the cathode and earth will supply some useful information concerning the fault. However, if the cathode voltage were measured first, an advantage might be gained. As the meter would already be set up to read voltages this would be quicker than measuring resistances and having to reset and zero the meter. Also measuring the cathode voltage will help us to narrow down the possible faulty area and so make a smaller number of resistance checks necessary.

Turn to *Frame 186.*

194

Yes, the reading of 190 volts would be acceptable.

The specified voltage was 175 volts with a tolerance of 10%. Therefore voltages 10% higher or lower than 175 volts are acceptable, and the tolerance range is between 157·5 volts and 192·5 volts. If no tolerance is given, then 10% is a reasonable working figure.

Now we return to the amplifier circuit. By measuring the anode and cathode voltages an open circuit was found between the anode and earth. What should be the next test, assuming that all voltage checks have been carried out?

A. Check the valve in a valve tester   *Frame 197*
B. Measure the resistance from cathode to earth   *Frame 199*
C. Measure resistance of R_K and C_K individually   *Frame 200*

Right. The resistance across the cathode by-pass capacitor should be infinity whether it is correct or on open circuit. If the cathode resistor was on open circuit, then the resistance across it would also be infinity. Therefore if the resistor was on open circuit and the capacitor was correct, we would not normally know which was giving the resistance reading. If the resistor was correct and the capacitor was either correct or on open circuit, the resistance reading from the cathode to earth would be the value of the cathode resistance. In this particular case, a reading of infinite resistance between the cathode and earth would in fact show that the cathode resistance was at fault. If the fault was the capacitor, then the resistor would also have to be on open circuit to give this reading, and we should assume that only one fault is occurring at a time.

However, in normal cases, a component must be isolated from the circuit before its resistance can be measured. It is not necessary to completely remove the component, unsoldering one connexion will be sufficient.

Also, ensure that the equipment is switched off before attempting any resistance checks.

Turn to *Frame 198*.

If you were given a specified voltage of 175 volts with a tolerance of 10%, then any voltage up to 10% above or below the specified voltage is allowable.

10% of 175 volts is 17·5 volts.

The upper tolerance limit will then be
175 volts plus 17·5 volts, which is 192·5 volts.

The lower tolerance limit will then be
175 volts minus 17·5 volts, which is 157·5 volts.

Therefore any voltage between 157·5 volts and 192·5 volts would be considered correct. The voltage as measured was 190 volts, which lies within the tolerance limits and therefore it is allowable.

Turn to *Frame 194*.

197

The valve should not be removed and tested until you are certain that it is at fault. There are several other components which could be the faulty one at this stage in your fault finding and therefore the valve should not be tested at this stage. There is often a tendency to check the valve in a faulty stage as the first step. This is very inefficient and you must not do this. Only check the valve when you have proved by your tests that it is the faulty component, or when there are no further checks you can perform.

Turn to *Frame 194* and try the question again.

198

One other very important point concerning resistance measurements is the type of meter used. It is of vital importance that the impedance of the meter is correct. It is not necessary to prove mathematically that this is so as you must already know this. When you measure resistances you are placing the impedance of the meter in parallel with the resistance which you are measuring. Unless the impedance of the meter is sufficiently high, the resistance of the circuit will be altered and the reading will be totally incorrect.

The type of meter required will vary with the resistance of the circuit itself, but as a precaution the highest possible impedance meter should be used if you are not certain of which type to use. Also the impedance of the meter will vary according to the scale setting, becoming higher with the higher scales. The highest possible scale should then be used to give the highest possible impedance but at the same time the scale must be low enough to ensure a reasonable deflexion. Any further information required on this subject will be found in any work on measurements.

Turn to *Frame 202*.

199

Correct. The first move in this case should be to measure the resistance from the cathode to earth. This will show whether the fault lies in the cathode circuit or in the valve.

If the resistance from the cathode to earth is infinity, then the fault lies in the cathode circuit, and the valve should be correct with no further check needed on it.

If the resistance from the cathode to earth is the value of the cathode resistor, then the fault does not lie in the cathode circuit, and the valve should be correct.

Note that this test does not check individual components.

Suppose that the resistance from the cathode to earth is infinity. What is the fault most likely to be?

A. The cathode resistor is on open circuit   *Frame 195*
B. Either the cathode resistor or the cathode by-pass capacitor could be on open circuit   *Frame 201*
C. The cathode by-pass capacitor is on open circuit   *Frame 204*

200

By measuring the resistances of R_K and C_K individually you would be eliminating certain components from the faulty area or finding the faulty component. However, you should not be testing individual components until you have narrowed down the faulty area as much as possible. There is a test you could carry out which would further decrease the possible faulty area. Think very carefully and try to determine this test.

Attempt the question again.

Turn to *Frame 194*.

201

You thought that either the cathode resistor or the cathode by-pass capacitor could be on open circuit when the resistance from the cathode to earth is infinity. This is not quite correct.

If the capacitor were on open circuit then this would not affect the static circuit as this capacitor is only used when a.c. signals are flowing through the valve. In any case, the resistance of the capacitor would be infinity whether it was correct or on open circuit. The resistance from the cathode to earth would then be the value of the cathode resistor.

If the fault is the capacitor, then we could only get this infinity resistance reading if the resistor also went open circuit at the samo time. For simplicity, we must assume that only one component goes faulty at any one time, unless the fault obviously makes more than one component faulty. Therefore the fault is not likely to be either the capacitor or the resistor, but should only be one of them.

Turn to *Frame 199* and have another attempt at the question.

202

Voltage and resistance checks should not be used until the faulty stage has been isolated. They should always enable the faulty component to be isolated. Do not leave this step in fault finding until the actual faulty component has definitely been isolated. Do not check components by substitution.

The sequence of steps for this stage of fault finding can be found on the flow chart at the end of the program.

Now turn to the next page for a review of this section.

Review of Voltage and Resistance Measurements

The fourth step in logical fault finding should be to carry out VOLTAGE AND RESISTANCE MEASUREMENTS.

The purpose of these measurements is to isolate a single faulty component.

This step should not be carried out until the fault has been isolated to a single stage by the use of signal injection or signal tracing.

The actual measurements taken will largely depend upon the stage and the fault in question. In general, start with measurements which will further isolate the faulty area, rather than to immediately commence the testing of individual components. In particular, Do NOT immediately test the valve in a faulty stage until voltage and resistance measurements have proved that this is the faulty component.

Try to avoid the individual testing of large numbers of components.

Now turn to the next page for the section test.

Test 4

Write down the answers to the following questions.

1. What is the name of the fourth step in logical fault finding?
2. What is the purpose of this step?
3. When is this step carried out?
4. What test equipment will be required for this step?
5. State the two measurements of this step in the order in which they should be carried out.
6. Which a.c. measurements could be taken as part of this step?
7. When should a valve be tested?
8. In a normal valve amplifier stage, which voltage should be checked first?
9. If no tolerance is stated, what is the amount of tolerance you should allow in your readings?

When you have written down the answers to these questions, turn to page *D* at the end of the book.

By this stage in the fault-finding method, the faulty component should have been isolated. When, and only when, the fault is known to be a certain component by the series of tests which have been carried out so far, then the fault can be repaired or the component replaced.

In the most efficient form of fault finding, only one component will require repair or replacement. If several components have to be tested by substitution, then the method has not been used correctly. The most common error in fault finding is to commence component replacement in a random fashion as soon as the faulty stage has been found, and sometimes before this stage is isolated. This is extremely time consuming, wasteful of materials, and most inefficient. Never replace a component in the hope that it might be faulty. You must know that a component *is* faulty before replacing it.

Turn to *Frame 205*.

204

It is impossible to say definitely at this stage that the fault is the by-pass capacitor. If this was the case, then the resistance from cathode to earth should be the value of the cathode resistor, and the value measured as infinity.

You are not thinking clearly. If you have difficulty in remembering the previous steps, then make a point in future of writing down the step and its result as you do it.

Now try the question again.

Turn to *Frame 199*.

205

It has been found that one of the most common errors in fault finding is to replace the valve as the first step in isolating the faulty component in a faulty stage. The valve should only be checked after it has been found to be the faulty component by the use of voltage and resistance checks. There are several faults which will affect the normal working of the valve, without damaging the valve at all. Replacing the valve will then have no effect.

It is also possible that although the valve is faulty, it was actually another fault which was causing this to occur. Replacing the valve will simply lead to another valve becoming defective.

In each case, the correct use of the steps in the fault-finding method which have been outlined in this program should have isolated the exact fault, without the need for substitution to check the fault. Moreover, the amount of time required for component replacing or valve testing is such that several conventional voltage and resistance checks could be performed and still show a saving in time. These should isolate the fault, and the fault finding would be more efficient as the fault should be found more quickly.

Turn to *Frame 206*.

206

Occasionally a regular fault develops on a particular equipment. Although experience shows which component to replace to get the equipment working correctly, this is no real solution. The real fault must lie elsewhere and an attempt must be made to isolate this. The fault may lie in the circuit design, in the supply of faulty components, or in a further component failure. Whatever the reason an attempt must be made to rectify this fault, as the repeated replacement of one component is very wasteful.

The sequence of steps for this stage of fault finding can be found on the flow chart at the end of the program.

Turn to *Frame 207*.

PERFORMANCE CHECKS

The steps which you have carried out so far should have isolated the fault and repaired or replaced the faulty component. The equipment should now be working correctly.

Are you now satisfied that the repair is complete?

A. Yes *Frame 209*
B. No *Frame 213*

208

Correct. Performance tests should be carried out as soon as possible after the step of repair or replacement. If the equipment is required immediately, and it appears to be functioning correctly, then performance tests could be left to a convenient time, but this should be as soon as possible.

Obviously if the performance test does not prove completely satisfactory then the fault has not been properly cleared, and you will have to start the fault-finding process again, using the loss in performance as the original symptom.

The sequence of steps for this stage of fault finding can be found on the flow chart at the end of the program.

Turn over a page for reviews of the two previous sections.

209

You said that when you had repaired or replaced the faulty component then the repair would be complete. This is not correct. Before you can be satisfied, the validity of the repair must be checked, as you may not in fact have completely repaired the fault.

Turn to *Frame 213*.

You have now covered the six basic steps of the fault-finding method. These steps are as follows:

1. Symptom analysis
2. Equipment inspection
3. Signal injection and signal tracing
4. Voltage and resistance checks
5. Repair and replacement
6. Performance tests

The order of these steps must be as shown.

All of these steps are shown on the flow chart at the end of the program. You may wish to revise from this chart before going on to the next section, which contains examples of fault finding on a superhet receiver.

When you are ready for these examples, turn to *Frame 212*.

Performance tests should be carried out immediately following the repair or replacement of the faulty component.

There may be occasions when the equipment is required immediately, and in this case the performance tests could be delayed for a short time. They should, however, be carried out as soon as possible.

Obviously if the performance test does not prove completely satisfactory then the fault has not been properly cleared, and you will have to start the fault-finding process again, using the loss in performance as the original symptom.

The sequence of steps for this stage of fault finding can be found on the flow chart at the end of the program.

Now turn to the next page for reviews of the two previous sections.

Review of Repair and Replacement

The fifth step in logical fault finding should be to REPAIR or REPLACE the faulty component which has been isolated by voltage and resistance measurements.

The purpose of this step is to rectify the fault determined by the previous steps.

Only one component should be repaired or replaced, assuming that only one component is faulty at any one time. Do not commence this step until the actual faulty component has been isolated by the preceding steps.

Review of Performance Tests

The sixth and final step in logical fault finding should be to carry out PERFORMANCE TESTS.

The purpose of these tests is to check the validity of the repair.

Never assume that the fault has been completely cured because one faulty component has been replaced. ALWAYS check the repair by carrying out a full series of performance tests.

If the performance tests are not satisfactory, then the fault has not been completely cured, and fault finding should commence again at the beginning of the method with the new symptoms.

Now turn to the next page for the test on these two sections.

Test 5

Write down the answers to the following questions.

1. What is the name of the fifth step in logical fault finding?
2. What is the purpose of this step?
3. How many times should this step have to be carried out?
4. What test equipment would be required for this step?
5. What is the name of the sixth step in logical fault finding?
6. What is the purpose of this step?
7. For a typical valve superhet receiver, which tests could be carried out as part of this step?
8. What should be done if this step is not completely successful?
9. When should this sixth step be carried out?
10. Could this sixth step ever be omitted?

When you have written down the answers to these questions, turn to page *E* at the end of the book.

The first examples are on the valve superhet whose circuit is given at the end of the program. You should be able to unfold this circuit, so that all the drawing is visible at the side of the book page, and pages can be turned whilst keeping the circuit in view.

The first fault is as follows. The immediately apparent symptoms are that there is no sound output from the receiver, and the gain control has no effect.

Equipment inspection shows that at least some of the valves are lit.

What should be your next step?

A. You would check the main fuse *Frame 214*
B. You would measure the h.t. voltage *Frame 216*
C. You would listen for hum in the speaker *Frame 218*

213

You were correct. The repair is not complete until performance tests have been performed on the equipment to check that the repair is satisfactory. In some very simple equipments it might be sufficient to check that there is an output in order to say that the repair is satisfactory, but usually more comprehensive performance tests should be needed.

When do you consider that performance tests should be performed?

- A. Immediately after the step of repair or replacement
  Frame 208
- B. At some convenient time after repair or replacement
  Frame 211

214

Your answer was that the first step should be to check the main fuse.

If the main fuse had blown, then the receiver would not give any output, and this was the symptom you were given. However, you were also told that some of the valves were lit, and therefore power must have been available to the receiver. Checking the main fuse would be a complete waste of time.

You must consider all the information you can gather together, and not only one item of information at a time.

Now turn to *Frame 212* and try the question again.

215

You said that you would check the h.t. supply. This is an unnecessary move as the fact that hum was present in the loudspeaker indicated that the audio frequency stages were functioning correctly. Therefore the h.t. should be correct.

The point of carrying out symptom analysis correctly is to eliminate the need for unnecessary tests.

Moreover, the sequence of steps you were given did not place voltage checks after symptom analysis.

You must apply the method correctly. Random testing will prove to be very inefficient.

If you wish to revise the method, turn to the flow sheet at the end of the program, then turn to *Frame 218* and use the method correctly.

216

Your answer was that you would measure the h.t. voltage as the first step in your fault-finding procedure.

Earlier in the program you were told that you must not carry out any detailed tests involving the use of test equipment, before pursuing symptom analysis and equipment inspection as far as possible. In this fault there was a very simple move which would give you more information concerning the fault, and which could be carried out without the use of any test equipment. Think carefully of what this could be, and then turn to *Frame 212.*

217

Your answer was that the next step after equipment inspection should be signal injection, to attempt to isolate the faulty stage if this has not already been found by the first two steps.

Where should the first test signal be injected?

A. At the aerial *Frame 219*
B. At the control grid of the intermediate frequency amplifier *Frame 221*
C. At the input to the second detector *Frame 224*

218

Correct. Listening for hum in the loudspeaker should be the first step.

A normal receiver which is functioning correctly will have a constant hum in the loudspeaker produced by mains ripple on the rectified h.t. This ripple is passed through the audio frequency stages if they are working normally, and the hum in the loudspeaker is a sign that the audio stages are in fact correct. If the audio frequency amplifiers are passing this ripple, then they must be receiving the correct power supplies, and therefore the power supply is most probably correct.

If there is no hum in the loudspeaker, then the audio frequency stages or the power stage are most likely to contain the fault.

Note that a simple item of symptom analysis has already cut down the possible faulty area. In this case there is no further symptom analysis which can be performed.

Assume that there was a normal hum present in the loudspeaker.

What should be your next step in attempting to isolate the fault?

A. Check the h.t. supply *Frame 215*
B. Carry out equipment inspection *Frame 220*
C. Carry out signal injection to isolate the faulty stage *Frame 222*

219

No. The signal should not be injected at the aerial. This will provide no new information.

Remember that in signal injection we always want to half-split the faulty area, not inject to the beginning of the faulty area or inject to the end of the faulty area.

Work out the faulty area of the receiver and then inject to its mid-point.

Where should the first test signal be injected?

   A. At the control grid of the intermediate frequency amplifier
      Frame 221
   B. At the input to the second detector   *Frame 226*

220

Correct. The next step after symptom analysis is equipment inspection, and this should be your next move.

In this fault no obvious defects are found by equipment inspection, but this step takes only a short while and it must be carried out each time the method is applied.

Now what should the next step be in attempting to isolate the fault?

   A. Perform signal injection in order to isolate the faulty stage   *Frame 217*
   B. Test the valves in the receiver   *Frame 223*
   C. Attempt to isolate the faulty component by carrying out voltage checks   *Frame 225*

221

The previous test showed that the audio frequency stages were most probably correct. Therefore the fault must lie in the receiver before the audio stages. The faulty area must lie between the aerial input and the second detector output. The centre of this area is the input to the intermediate frequency amplifier, and this is where the first test signal should be injected, using the half-split method.

In this receiver the time to be saved by the use of the half-split method is not very great, but you should still use this method to accustom yourself to its use.

Remember that in this program you do not need to know the correct signal input, or to tune to the signal if this is required. In an actual fault-finding situation, do not confuse a receiver giving no output because of an incorrect input signal with a defective receiver. The correct signal in this test would be the intermediate frequency, amplitude modulated with a 1 kHz audio frequency.

When this signal is injected to the control grid of the inter-mediate frequency amplifier, a normal output is heard from the loudspeaker.

Where should the next test signal be injected?

- A. At the input to the second detector   *Frame 227*
- B. At the control grid of the mixer valve   *Frame 229*
- C. At the aerial input socket   *Frame 231*

222

You said that you would now carry out signal injection in order to isolate the faulty stage. This is not correct. You have omitted a step in the fault-finding method.

Turn to *Frame 218* and answer the question again, following the exact method you have been given. This will prove to be the most efficient.

E

223

Your answer was that you would now test all the valves in the receiver. You must not do this. This is a very bad and inefficient method of fault finding. You may test one valve later in the method if you have found evidence that the valve is probably faulty. Meanwhile, keep exactly to the method which you have been taught. The previous step was equipment inspection, and you should easily remember which step came after this. If you cannot remember, turn to the flow sheet at the end of the program, and revise the method.

Try the question again.

Turn to *Frame 220*.

224

Your answer was that the first test signal should be injected to the input of the second detector. This is not correct.

The result of the previous tests showed that the a.f. stages were most probably correct, as there was a normal hum in the speaker. The faulty area therefore lies before the a.f. stages and the test signal should be injected to the mid-point of this faulty area.

Turn to *Frame 217* and try the question again.

225

You said that you would now attempt to isolate the faulty component by carrying out voltage checks. This step is out of order in the fault-finding method.

The previous test was to carry out equipment inspection.

Think carefully which step comes after equipment inspection and then attempt the question again.

Turn to *Frame 220*.

226

No. The signal should not be injected to the input of the second detector.

The result of the previous tests showed that the a.f. stages were most probably correct, since there was a normal hum in the speaker. The faulty area therefore lies before the a.f. stages and the test signal should be injected to the mid-point of this faulty area. The mid-point of the faulty area is the control grid of the intermediate frequency amplifier, and the first test signal should be injected to this point.

Turn to *Frame 221*.

227

The first test signal was injected to the control grid of the intermediate frequency amplifier, and the output was then normal.

Therefore all parts of the circuit after the control grid input of the intermediate frequency amplifier are correct, and the fault must lie before this point. You said that the next signal should be injected at the input of the second detector, a stage which has been proved correct by the previous test.

You must think very carefully of the results of all the previous tests. If you cannot remember them all then make a list, as this will always prove useful.

Now try the question again.

Turn to *Frame 221*.

228

The previous step isolated the mixer as the faulty stage. Now you have to find the faulty component in the faulty stage, but you should never do this by checking each component in the circuit as you suggested.

The step in the fault-finding method which will isolate the faulty component in the faulty stage is to carry out voltage and resistance checks. Remember that the step of signal injection or signal tracing isolates the faulty stage and the next step is to carry out these voltage and resistance checks.

Turn to *Frame 235*.

229

Correct. The fact that there was a normal output when a signal was injected to the intermediate frequency amplifier proves that the stages of the intermediate frequency amplifier, and the second detector, are correct, and confirms that the audio frequency stages are correct. Therefore the fault must lie before the intermediate frequency amplifier. The possible faulty stages are now the mixer and the local oscillator.

Half-splitting this faulty area means injecting to the control grid of the mixer stage. Remember that it is best to inject the intermediate frequency at this point because this will prove which stage is at fault without the need for tuning or for using two signal generators.

No output is heard from the loudspeaker when the intermediate frequency is injected to the control grid of the mixer valve.

Which stage is most likely to contain the fault?

    A. The mixer stage   *Frame 232*
    B. The local oscillator stage   *Frame 234*
    C. The fault could be in either stage   *Frame 236*

230

Once the faulty stage had been isolated you wished to further isolate the faulty area by using signal injection to half-split the mixer stage. This is a reasonable move, but will not always prove to be an advantage.

It is better to go straight on to voltage and resistance checks as soon as the faulty stage has been isolated.

Turn to *Frame 235*.

231

You were told that a normal output from the speaker was obtained when a test signal was injected at the control grid of the intermediate frequency amplifier.

Therefore the stages after this point must be correct, and the fault must lie before this point. The faulty area should then be half-split, and a test signal injected at the mid-point. In fact by injecting to the aerial you injected to the beginning of the faulty stage, and not the middle.

Now try the question again.

Turn to *Frame 221*.

232

Correct. The faulty stage is most likely to be the mixer stage. As an additional check, the local oscillator could be tested very simply by measuring the d.c. voltage from the control grid of the local oscillator valve to earth. This grid leakage voltage is found to be correct, confirming that the local oscillator stage is correct and that the fault is most likely to lie in the mixer stage.

What should be the next step in the fault-finding method?

- A. Check each component in the mixer stage *Frame 228*
- B. Use signal injection to split the mixer stage *Frame 230*
- C. Carry out voltage and resistance checks in the mixer stage *Frame 235*

233

Right. The first test within the mixer stage should be to check the anode voltage.

This is given as 200 volts in the test data, and you measure it to be 181 volts.

Do you consider that this voltage is correct or not?

    A. It is correct   *Frame 238*
    B. It is not correct   *Frame 240*

234

No output was heard from the loudspeaker when the intermediate frequency was injected to the control grid of the mixer valve. The fault had previously been isolated to either the mixer stage or the local oscillator stage. Injecting normal r.f. signals does not prove which of these two stages is at fault, but injecting the intermediate frequency to the mixer valve proves whether or not the mixer stage itself is operating correctly.

In this case there was no output from this test. Therefore the mixer stage is the faulty stage, and not the local oscillator.

Turn to *Frame 232*.

235

Once the faulty stage has been isolated, the next step in the fault-finding method is to carry out voltage and resistance checks in the faulty stage, in this case in the mixer stage.

However, as explained earlier in the program, the stage could be split by injecting a test signal at the anode of the mixer valve, thus halving the faulty area. The correct test frequency would be the intermediate frequency, amplitude modulated with an audio frequency, usually 1 kHz. If this signal is injected, the output is found to be normal.

Ignore this last injection to the anode of the mixer valve and use the method of voltage and resistance checks for this example.

What should be the first test within the mixer stage?

A. Check the anode voltage of the mixer valve *Frame 233*
B. Check the cathode voltage of the mixer valve *Frame 237*
C. Measure the resistance from the cathode of the mixer valve to earth *Frame 239*

236

The purpose of this test was to isolate the fault to either the mixer or the local oscillator stage. The result you were given was sufficient for you to make this decision.

You should be able to give the correct answer to this question, using the information you were given on the previous frame. Now turn to *Frame 229* and answer the question again.

237

There is little to choose between measuring the cathode voltage first or the anode voltage first. Usually, more information will be obtained if the first voltage is the anode voltage, and this is followed by the cathode voltage.

Turn to *Frame 233*.

238

The specified voltage was 200 volts, but you were not given any tolerance level. In these circumstances the program taught you to take a tolerance of 10%, which is 20 volts. Therefore any voltage between 180 and 220 volts is allowable, and your answer was correct.

Since the anode voltage is the correct value, which part of the mixer circuit must be correct?

A. The mixer circuit between the h.t. and earth through the valve is correct   *Frame 241*
B. The mixer circuit above the anode is correct   *Frame 243*
C. The mixer circuit below the anode is correct   *Frame 245*

239

No. Voltage checks should be carried out before starting on resistance checks.

Now decide which voltage should be measured first, and then answer the question on *Frame 233*.

240

200 volts was given as the specified voltage and you measured it as 181 volts. The tolerance given was 10%.

The upper allowable limit would be 10% above 200 volts, and the lower allowable limit would be 10% below 200 volts.

Therefore any voltage between 220 volts and 180 volts is considered to be correct, and 181 volts would be considered normal.

Turn to *Frame 238*.

241

If the anode voltage is the correct value, then most probably the mixer circuit between the h.t. and earth through the valve is correct.

What should be your next step?

A. Measure the resistance from cathode to earth *Frame 244*
B. Measure the resistance from the control grid to earth *Frame 246*
C. Measure the grid bias *Frame 248*

242

You said that you would check the control grid potential by measuring the potential between the control grid and the cathode. This is correct. However, the bias could also be checked by measuring the voltage across the cathode resistor, as the bias in this circuit is auto-cathode bias.

Turn to *Frame 254.*

243

Your answer was that since the anode voltage was correct, the mixer circuit between the h.t. and the anode is correct. This is partly correct.

In fact the mixer circuit between the h.t. and earth through the valve must be correct. If there was a short circuit to earth at some point between the anode and earth, then the anode voltage would either be very low or zero, depending upon the exact position of the short. Similarly if there was an open circuit at any point below the anode then the valve would not be conducting, and the anode voltage would be equal to the h.t. voltage.

Turn to *Frame 241.*

244

Your answer was that the next step would be to measure the resistance from the cathode to earth. This is not correct.

The previous test had proved that the circuit between the h.t. and earth through the valve was correct. There is therefore no point in measuring the resistance from the cathode to earth.

Turn to *Frame 241* and try the question again.

245

Your answer was that since the anode voltage is correct, the mixer circuit between the anode and earth is correct. This is partly correct.

If the anode voltage is correct then all of the circuit between the h.t. and earth through the valve must be correct.

Turn to *Frame 241*.

246

If the cathode was found to be correct then it is a good idea to check the control grid next. However, it will be easier to measure the control grid bias before measuring the resistance from the control grid to earth as the meter will already be set up to measure voltages.

Turn to *Frame 248*.

If the secondary winding of the transformer **T1** was on short circuit, the resistance from the control grid to earth would still not be zero. The fault must be providing a direct path to earth from the control grid.

Study the circuit and try to find which component could do this, then turn to *Frame 254* and try the question again.

Correct. The next step would be to measure the grid bias. Remember that this voltage should be measured across the cathode resistor. It is found to be 3 volts, which is the correct value. However, this does not mean that the control grid is at the correct potential with respect to the cathode.

How could you check if the control grid was at the correct potential?

 A. Measure the potential between the control grid and the cathode   *Frame 242*
 B. Measure the resistance from the control grid to earth *Frame 250*
 C. Measure the potential between the control grid and earth *Frame 252*

249

Correct. The fault is most likely to be either capacitor C1 or capacitor C3 on short circuit. These are the only components which have a direct connexion to earth, and if they went on short circuit then there would be zero resistance between the control grid and earth.

To find the actual faulty component, each capacitor would have to be disconnected in turn and the resistance to earth measured.

Whichever capacitor was at fault would now require replacement and the receiver should then operate normally.

When this is done, is the repair completed?

    A. Yes *Frame 253*
    B. No *Frame 255*

250

You said that you would check the control grid potential by measuring the resistance from the control grid to earth. This is a necessary step, but not at this point. Firstly the potential must be checked.

Turn to *Frame 242* and try the question again.

251

If the capacitor C2 was on short circuit, the resistance from the control grid to earth would still not be zero. The fault must be providing a direct path to earth from the control grid.

Study the circuit and try to find which component could do this, then turn to *Frame 254* and try the question again.

252

You said that you would check the control grid potential by measuring the potential between the control grid and earth. This is not correct. You should know from your theory that the only voltage present across the resistance between the control grid and earth is the grid leak current. This test does not measure the grid bias.

Turn to *Frame 248* and try the question again.

253

You have repaired the fault, but to be certain of your repair you must carry out performance tests as soon as possible.

Turn to *Frame 255.*

254

You could check that the control grid was at the correct potential with respect to the cathode by measuring the potential between the control grid and the cathode. However, you could also check that the grid was at the correct potential by measuring the resistance from the control grid to earth. If this resistance is correct, and the voltage across the cathode resistor is correct, then the control grid should be at the correct potential with respect to the cathode.

Assume that you do this by checking the resistance between the control grid and earth. This is found to be zero, and therefore the control grid was not at the correct potential.

You should now be able to make an estimate of the actual fault.

What do you consider the fault to be?

A. The secondary winding of transformer T1 is on short circuit *Frame 247*

B. Either capacitor C1 or capacitor C3 is on short circuit *Frame 249*

C. Capacitor C2 is on short circuit *Frame 251*

255

Correct. As soon as the repair has been made, performance tests should be carried out, and therefore the fault is not completely cleared by simply replacing the component. This would be particularly useful in this case as the component replaced was a tuning capacitor, and not a smoothing or decoupling capacitor. There is a reasonable chance that the new capacitor will not operate in exactly the same way.

You have now completed the first problem on fault finding and you should begin to observe how the method, which you learnt as separate steps, actually ties together in practice.

Proceed now to Valve Problem No. 2 which concerns a fault of a different nature from the one you have just identified.

Turn to *Frame 256*.

VALVE PROBLEM NO.2

Here is the second problem on the valve superhet receiver. The fault is as follows. The output is normal except that there is also a lot of noise.

This is a different type of fault to the one in the last example. The previous fault could be called a *catastrophic* fault as the output of the receiver broke down completely. This fault is of a type which could be called *non-catastrophic* as the output is still present. There is a third type of fault which is called *intermittent,* as the fault is only present for part of the time. This fault is the hardest of all to clear, as you can never be certain that your repair has cured the symptoms; it could be that the fault has temporarily cleared itself and will return later.

Now to return to the fault in question. You were told that the output was normal except for the addition of a large amount of noise.

What should be your first step in attempting to find this fault?

A. Disconnect the aerial and see how the noise is affected
Frame 258
B. Vary the gain control and see how the noise is affected
Frame 260
C. Tap each valve in turn and see how the noise is affected
Frame 262

257

No, this is not correct. Signal injection when attempting to isolate a fault producing noise is not a good step. Wherever the signal is injected, the faulty stage will still be producing the noise, and as all stages are working the noise will be included in the output. Therefore the signal injection will give no new information on the whereabouts of the fault.

Try the question again.

Turn to *Frame 260*.

258

Your answer was that you would disconnect the aerial and see how the noise is affected. This is a useful test as it should prove whether the noise is being produced within the receiver or whether it is external to the receiver. There will be no point in carrying out tests on the receiver if the noise is external. However, this is a test, and there is a simpler move which should be carried out first. This is to vary the gain control; since it will only take a few seconds it is best to carry out this move first.

Turn to *Frame 260*.

259

You probably arrived at the answer of signal tracing in desperation, as you would do in an actual fault-finding problem. Monitoring signals is not a good method to use to trace noise faults at this stage of your fault finding. Therefore another method of tracing noisy stages is required.

Turn to *Frame 264*.

260

Your answer was that you would vary the gain control and see how the noise was affected. This is correct.

This test is performing symptom analysis which is the first step in the fault-finding method. You should remember that varying the gain control was quoted as an example of how to obtain extra symptoms.

In this case the result of this move will show whether the fault is before the gain control, or after the gain control, and this will cut down the possible faulty area. If the noise volume varies as the gain control is varied, then the fault producing the noise is before the gain control, and may in fact be a fault outside the equipment. If the noise volume does not vary as the gain control is varied, then the fault producing the noise is after the gain control. This very simple move has cut down the faulty area substantially.

The result of this test is that when the gain control is varied, the noise output varies with it.

What should be the next step?

A. Inject a test signal to the control grid of the intermediate frequency amplifier *Frame 257*
B. Monitor the signal at the second detector *Frame 263*
C. Disconnect aerial and short out its terminals *Frame 265*

261

No. Signal injection will not help to find the stage which is producing the noise. Wherever the signal is injected, the faulty stage will still be producing the noise, and as all stages are functioning, this noise would appear at the speaker.

You must think more carefully.

Turn to *Frame 265* and make another attempt at the question.

262

Your answer was that you would tap each valve in turn and see how the noise is affected. This is a move which is sometimes carried out when there is noise in the output. The valves are a likely cause of noise, and tapping them should affect the noise. However, the noise is not definitely produced by a valve, and even if it was this test is not guaranteed to find the faulty valve. Therefore this would not be a good move.

Try the question again.

Turn to *Frame 256*.

263

You said that you would monitor the output of the second detector. This may give you further information on the fault, but it is unlikely. Monitoring signals is a possible way of determining where the noise is produced, but is not within the scope of this work.

Try the question again.

Turn to *Frame 260*.

264

Right. Signal tracing in the receiver will help to find out where the noise is being produced. Signal injection cannot be used as this will not help to isolate the fault. Wherever the signal is injected, the faulty stage will still be producing the noise and this will appear in the output.

Unfortunately you may not be able to carry out signal tracing because of shortage of equipment or other reasons, and you must then have an alternative method of discovering which stage is producing the noise. This can be done quite simply.

Our tests so far have isolated the faulty stage to be one of the mixer, local oscillator, intermediate frequency amplifier, or second detector stages. Suppose that the valve in the intermediate frequency amplifier is removed and the noise in the output is still present.

Which is the stage which contains the fault?

A. The mixer stage   *Frame 266*
B. The intermediate frequency amplifier stage   *Frame 268*
C. The second detector stage   *Frame 270*

265

Correct. The next move should be to disconnect the aerial and short out its terminals. This will show whether the fault lies within the receiver or is being produced externally. Although it may be thought that this step should be carried out first of all this is not so. This test involves the dismantling of a component, whereas the varying of the gain control would only take a few seconds.

Now let us assume that the noise remains when the aerial is shorted out.

What should be the next step?

A. Carry out signal tracing   *Frame 259*
B. Carry out signal injection   *Frame 261*
C. Carry out voltage and resistance checks   *Frame 267*

266

The mixer stage could not contain the fault producing the noise in this case. When the valve in the intermediate frequency amplifier was removed, then the intermediate frequency stage was rendered inoperative. Therefore no signals from this stage, or from previous stages, could reach the output. The noise was still present and therefore must be produced in a stage after the intermediate frequency amplifier stage.

Turn to *Frame 270*.

267

Your answer was that you would now carry out voltage and resistance checks. This should eventually find the fault but this move would be very inefficient as you do not yet know which is the faulty stage.

Turn to *Frame 265* and make another attempt at the question.

268

The intermediate frequency amplifier could not contain the fault producing the noise in this case. When the valve was removed from the intermediate frequency stage, this stage was rendered inoperative. Therefore no signals from this stage could reach the output. The noise was still present in the output and therefore must be produced in a stage after the intermediate frequency amplifier stage.

Turn to *Frame 270*.

269

Right. The next step would be to remove the mixer valve, making certain that the amplifier valve and the detector valve had been replaced.

If the noise stops when this valve is removed, then the fault lies in either the mixer or the local oscillator stage. If the noise is still present in the output, then the fault lies in the intermediate frequency amplifier stage.

If the noise did stop when the mixer valve was removed, then the next step would be to replace the mixer valve and remove the local oscillator valve. If the noise then stops the fault lies in the local oscillator stage, and if the noise does not stop then the fault lies in the mixer stage.

Once the faulty stage has been found, then of course the next step is to isolate the faulty component in the faulty stage by the use of voltage and resistance checks. There is no particular advantage to be gained from pursuing this fault, as you have already seen how to carry out voltage and resistance checks within a stage. However, this method of removing the valves to track down a stage producing noise is very useful, and you should make a note of this.

Now if you turn to *Frame 274* you will find the final example on the valve superhet.

Correct, the fault must lie in the second detector.

As the valve was removed from the intermediate frequency amplifier this stage cannot be working, and no signal from any previous stage can be passed. The audio frequency amplifier stages have already been proved correct, and therefore the fault must lie in the detector.

However, if the noise content of the output had ceased when the valve from the intermediate frequency amplifier was removed, the fault must lie in another stage.

Which stage would now be most likely to contain the fault?

A. The mixer stage   *Frame 272*
B. The local oscillator stage   *Frame 275*
C. The intermediate frequency amplifier stage   *Frame 276*
D. Either the mixer, the local oscillator or the intermediate frequency amplifier stages   *Frame 278*

Removing the local oscillator valve would indicate which stage was at fault, but it would be more logical to remove the mixer valve first.

Turn to *Frame 269*.

272

The faulty stage could be the mixer, but it could also be the local oscillator stage or the intermediate frequency amplifier stage. When the valve was removed from the intermediate frequency stage, no noise produced in the earlier stages could pass through the intermediate stage, and there could be no noise produced in the intermediate stage itself. Therefore, when there is no noise in the output when this valve is removed, it does not tell us which stage contains the fault; it only tells us that the second detector stage is functioning normally.

Turn to *Frame 278*.

273

Carrying out voltage and resistance checks on the three possible faulty stages would eventually find the fault. However, this is a very inefficient way of proceeding. As the method of removing valves in successive stages has proved very efficient so far, why not pursue this test as far as possible?

Try the question again.

Turn to *Frame 278*.

VALVE PROBLEM NO.3

Here is the third example on the superhet receiver, using the valve circuit.

The fault symptoms are that the receiver does not pick up any signals.

What should be your first step in isolating the fault?

A.   Listen for hum in the loudspeaker   *Frame 277*
B.   Check the h.t. fuse   *Frame 279*
C.   Measure the value of the h.t. supply at the test point
     Frame 281

275

The faulty stage could be the local oscillator, but it could also be the mixer or the intermediate frequency amplifier stage. When the valve was removed from the intermediate frequency stage, no noise produced in the earlier stages could pass through the intermediate stage, and there could be no noise produced in the intermediate stage itself. Therefore when there is no noise in the output when this valve is removed, it does not tell us which stage contains the fault; it only tells us that the second detector stage is functioning normally.

Turn to *Frame 278*.

276

The faulty stage could be the intermediate frequency amplifier, but it could also be the mixer stage or the local oscillator stage. When the valve was removed from the intermediate frequency stage there would be no noise produced in this stage. However, if there was any noise in the previous stages this could not pass through the intermediate stage. Therefore, when there is no noise output in the speaker when the intermediate frequency amplifier valve is removed, it does not tell us which stage contains the fault; it only tells us that the second detector stage is functioning normally.

Turn to *Frame 278*.

277

Correct. You should listen for hum in the loudspeaker. This is carrying out symptom analysis which you were taught was the first step in fault finding with the logical method given in this program. You have already been told that there will be hum in the loudspeaker if the audio frequency stages are functioning normally. This hum is produced by the mains ripple on the h.t. supply.

In this particular case there is no output of any sort from the loudspeaker.

What should be your next step in isolating the fault?

A. Check the main fuse   *Frame 280*
B. Check if power is available by testing the valves to see if they are lit or warm   *Frame 282*
C. Measure the value of the h.t. supply at the test point D *Frame 284*

278

Correct. The fault could lie in any of these three stages, but we would be certain that the fault did not lie in the second detector stage.

How then could you determine which stage contains the fault?

A. By removing the mixer valve   *Frame 269*
B. By removing the local oscillator valve   *Frame 271*
C. By carrying out voltage and resistance checks in the three possible faulty stages   *Frame 273*

279

Your answer was that the first step to isolate the fault should be to check the h.t. fuse. This is a possible cause of the fault symptom given, but there could be many other possible causes. There is a much simpler way of checking that the h.t. supply is normal. You have already been told what this move should be. Think very carefully of possible symptom analysis of the fault and try the question again.

Turn to *Frame 274.*

No, you should not check the main fuse at this point. You have not pursued symptom analysis as far as you can, and there is a simpler method of checking whether mains power is available. Remember that symptom analysis is only going to take a very short while, and that the time spent in doing this will be more than saved by the information it will provide.

Although the main fuse could be the possible cause of this fault, it is not the only possible cause, and therefore you should not check it at this point. You should have searched for another symptom of the fault, and there is a very simple move which will give information on the main power supply to the receiver. This would be to check the valves by looking to see if they were lit, or feeling them to see if they were warm. If they were, then the main fuse must be correct. If they were not then the main fuse is very probably at fault.

Turn to *Frame 282*.

Your answer was that the first step to isolate the fault should be to measure the value of the h.t. supply at the test point D. This is not correct. Remember that you should not carry out any special tests, or measure voltages, until symptom analysis and equipment inspection have been pursued as far as possible. The fault could lie in the h.t. supply, but there are also many other possible faults.

However, there is another method of checking that the h.t. supply is normal without measuring the voltage or carrying out any other tests. You have already been told what this move should be. Think very carefully of possible symptom analysis of the fault and then try the question again.

Turn to *Frame 274*.

282

Correct. You would endeavour to discover more symptoms by checking the valves to see if they were lit or warm. This will show whether power is available to the receiver without the need for special measurements.

The result of this test is that all valves are warm and lit. The previous information gained was that the receiver does not pick up any signals and there is no output at all from the loudspeaker.

Which area of the receiver is most likely to contain the fault?

A. The audio frequency stages *Frame 285*
B. The h.t. supply *Frame 287*
C. The area before the audio frequency stages *Frame 289*
D. Either the audio frequency stages or the h.t. supply *Frame 291*

283

Correct. Checking the value of the h.t. voltage at the test point D should be the next step. This is not the step after symptom analysis and equipment inspection, but the special circumstances of this fault necessitates checking the voltage before signal injection.

There are therefore exceptions to the rules of fault finding which you were given in the first part of this program. With experience you will discover when these exceptions will be allowable. Until you gain this experience keep exactly to the order of the method which you were taught. With the method given you will *always* find the fault, and in this particular case injecting the test signal would only add one extra step to the fault finding.

Now to proceed with finding this particular fault.

When the h.t. voltage at the test point D is measured it is found to be 210 volts. What should be the next step in finding the fault?

A. Inject a test signal to the control grid of the audio frequency voltage amplifier *Frame 290*
B. Inject a test signal to the loudspeaker *Frame 292*
C. Inject a test signal to the anode of the audio frequency power amplifier *Frame 294*

284

You said that you would now measure the value of the h.t. supply at the test point D. This is not correct.

Although the fault could be that the h.t. supply was not correct, there are several other possible faults. Before carrying out any specialized tests you should pursue symptom analysis as far as possible. The time taken for this will only be at the most a few minutes, and this will be more than saved by the information it will provide.

Think very carefully to discover another step in symptom analysis which would provide further information on the fault.

Turn to *Frame 277* and try the question again.

285

Correct. The fault could lie in the audio frequency stages, but there is an equal chance that it lies in the h.t. supply. Either of these would fit the symptoms we have discovered so far equally well.

Turn to *Frame 291*.

286

Your answer was that you would inject a test signal to the control grid of the second audio frequency amplifier. This could be a wasted move. The symptom analysis carried out so far has proved that the fault lies either in the second audio frequency stage or in the h.t. supply. Whichever was the actual fault, a test signal injected to the second audio stage would produce no output, and would give no new information concerning the fault. This test could, however, be carried out quickly as a confirmation of the previous symptom analysis.

You should not waste time in carrying out unnecessary tests. Symptom analysis is designed to save these unwanted steps.

Now think very carefully of the information you have now gathered concerning the fault, and consider what should be the next step to isolate the fault.

Turn to *Frame 291* and attempt the question again.

287

Correct. The fault could lie in the h.t. supply, but there is also a chance that it lies in the audio frequency stages. Nothing we have found out so far in the symptom analysis shows that it is definitely one or the other.

Turn to *Frame 291*.

288

Although the loudspeaker is a possible fault, you would not be justified in injecting a test signal to it at this stage in your fault finding. Remember that you do not test individual components until you are certain that they could be faulty. In this case you are not at all certain that the loudspeaker is at fault, and this should not be checked, especially as this is not a usual type of fault.

Try the question again.　　Turn to *Frame 291*.

289

You said that the fault most likely lay before the audio frequency stages. This is not correct. If the fault was in the area you stated then the audio frequency stages would be correct, and they would produce a hum in the loudspeaker. This hum was not present.

Try the question again.　　Turn to *Frame 282*.

290

No. Injecting a test signal to the control grid of the audio frequency voltage amplifier would be a completely wrong move. You know already that the fault cannot lie in this stage and therefore carrying out tests on this stage will be a complete waste of time. You must think more carefully before you decide which step to take.

Try the question again.   Turn to *Frame 283*.

291

Correct. The fault lies either in the audio frequency stages or in the h.t. supply. It is possible to go a little further than this. If the second audio frequency amplifier and the loudspeaker were correct then there would be some hum in the speaker, regardless of whether the first audio frequency amplifier was functioning. Since there was no hum at all in the loudspeaker, the fault must now lie in either the second audio frequency stage or the h.t. supply.

What should be the next step to isolate the fault?

A. Check the h.t. voltage at the test point   *Frame 283*
B. Inject a test signal to the control grid of the second audio frequency amplifier   *Frame 286*
C. Inject a test signal to the loudspeaker   *Frame 288*

292

You said that you would inject a test signal to the loudspeaker. This is a possible faulty component which could give the symptoms which we have discovered. However, you have been told never to test individual components until you have discovered which component is most likely to be faulty by carrying out logical tests. Injecting to the speaker could find the fault, but it would not be the most efficient method of doing this. Try to be more logical in your fault finding.

Turn to *Frame 283* and make another attempt at the question.

293

No. You should not replace the capacitor C15. The fault is not definitely this component.

The actual faulty component should be isolated by carrying out voltage and resistance checks before any replacements are made.

Turn to *Frame 298*.

294

Correct. The next step should be to inject a test signal at the anode of the audio frequency power amplifier.

Once the h.t. voltage had been proved to be correct, the faulty area was narrowed down to the audio frequency power amplifier, including the loudspeaker. Injecting to the anode of this stage is half-splitting the faulty area, which is the method you were taught. Care must be taken when injecting to the anode of a stage as there is h.t. present at this point. Unless the signal generator has a d.c. blocking capacitor in the output, you should connect in a suitable size of capacitor on the output lead of the generator to protect it from the large voltage at the anode.

When the test signal is injected to the anode of the audio frequency power amplifier, there is no output from the loudspeaker.

What should be your next move?

- A. Inject a test signal to the loudspeaker *Frame 296*
- B. Inject a test signal to the matching transformer *Frame 297*
- C. Check the anode voltage of the audio frequency power amplifier valve *Frame 299*

295

No. You should not replace the transformer. The fault is not definitely this component and to replace a transformer would take a reasonably long time, besides being a possible waste of a component if the fault was the capacitor.

The actual faulty component of the two possible faults should be isolated by carrying out voltage and resistance checks in the faulty area.

Turn to *Frame 298*.

296

Injecting to the loudspeaker would now be a reasonable move.

As there was no output when the test signal was injected to the anode, then the number of possible faulty components is now small enough to allow individual tests to be made.

However, you could carry on with the logical half-splitting. Try this method and give another answer on *Frame 294*.

297

Correct. Signal injection can be pursued by injecting a test signal to the matching transformer.

When the signal is injected to the secondary winding, the output is normal, but when it is injected to the primary winding there is no output.

This has narrowed down the fault to two possible components, the primary winding of the matching transformer or the capacitor C15.

What should be the next step?

- A. Replace capacitor C15   *Frame 293*
- B. Replace the matching transformer T6   *Frame 295*
- C. Carry out resistance checks on capacitor C15 and transformer T6   *Frame 298*

298

Correct. You should carry out resistance checks on the two possible faulty components to discover which is the actual faulty component. The faults expected with the results of the tests carried out so far are either a short circuit across the capacitor C15 or the primary winding of the transformer T6, or an open circuit on the primary winding of transformer T6. Once the faulty component has definitely been isolated it can be replaced. Performance tests should then be carried out to check the validity of the repair.

You have now completed the last example on the valve superhet receiver.

Turn to *Frame 300*.

299

You said that you would now check the anode voltage of the audio frequency power amplifier valve. This would be correct if you had done as much signal injection as possible. However, signal injection can be pursued one step further, and this will be very easy as you already have the signal generator set up to give the correct test signal.

Assuming that you are going to carry on with signal injection, answer the question on *Frame 294* again.

F

The next section deals with examples of fault finding on the transistorized superhet receiver whose circuit is given at the end of the program. Do not go on to this section if you do not have a basic knowledge of the operation of transistorized circuits.

If you wish to work through these examples turn to *Frame 301*.

301

Before dealing with the actual examples, there are several specialized aspects of fault finding in transistorized circuits which will be discussed. These special considerations do not alter the basic method of fault finding in any way, they are simply examples of special tests, and only a few common examples can be included here.

The main differences between fault finding in valve circuits and transistor circuits are that the elements of the transistor are in actual physical contact, whereas the electrodes of a valve are separated by an insulator; and the potentials used in transistor circuits are usually less than 10 volts, whereas the h.t. potential in a valve circuit is usually in excess of 200 volts. There are also two types of transistor, the *npn* and the *pnp* transistor. To date the *pnp* transistor has been used most widely employing circuits which may be termed positive earth circuits. However, *npn* transistors are now coming into wider use, and these employ circuits which may be termed negative earth circuits. Care will be needed with the polarity of voltage measurements in the two types of circuit.

The following examples use a well known commercial receiver employing *pnp* transistors and, as can be seen from the circuit, a positive earth is used.

As a transistor is heat and light sensitive, special precautions have to be taken. Normally no difficulty should arise through the transistor being light sensitive because it is encapsulated during manufacture in an opaque container. However, considerable difficulty may be experienced with the heat-sensitive property of a transistor, especially if great care is not taken during soldering.

Turn to *Frame 302*.

302

When measuring the voltages around a transistor much smaller readings are obtained than in a valve circuit. For example, in the circuit given at the end of the program, the first intermediate frequency amplifier, using transistor G2, has the following specified voltages

Emitter	0·7 volt
Base	0·8 volt
Collector	7 volts

Taking a tolerance of 10% in these readings, the emitter voltage must lie between 0·77 volt and 0·63 volt, therefore a measured voltage of approximately 1 volt is not accurate enough. A difference of 0·1 volt would then be significant in the emitter voltage, but would not be significant in the collector voltage where the same tolerance of 10% allows a variation of 0·7 volt. Obviously a multimeter with small scale values is required, and the impedance of the meter must still be high at these low ranges.

Remember also that because the elements of the transistor are in physical contact, and the barrier potential is very small at the junctions, an open circuit on one element does not preclude a potential being present.

Turn to *Frame 303*.

303

The next point of difficulty is the measurement of resistance. A meter measures the resistance between two points by applying a known voltage and measuring the current flow. The size of this applied voltage is of the order of the potentials in the transistor circuit, and may be larger. For example, suppose that you wished to measure the resistance from the base of G4 transistor to earth in the circuit given at the end of the program. This would apply the test voltage of the meter across the base-emitter junction and the resistor R15 in series. As the base-emitter potential is of the order of $0 \cdot 1$ volt in this stage, the applied potential would certainly be much larger than this and could cause an excess current to flow through the transistor. Whether or not this current actually does flow will depend upon whether the applied potential from the meter provides forward or reverse bias for the emitter-base junction. If the bias was reverse then the transistor would be protected, but if the bias was forward, runaway would almost certainly be a possibility and this could permanently damage the transistor.

You should therefore ensure that when a potential is applied during resistance measurements, it reverse biases the junction of the transistor across which it is applied.

A much safer move is to disconnect the transistor from the circuit before carrying out resistance checks. It is not always necessary to completely disconnect the transistor, and in most cases disconnecting the base connexion will be a sufficient safeguard.

Turn to *Frame 304*.

304

Another difficulty is encountered with signal injection. When a test signal is injected to the base of a transistor, the test voltage is being applied across the base-emitter junction and the resistance in the base lead and the emitter lead. In certain cases this voltage could be dangerously high. To ensure that this does not occur, always start with lowest possible output of the signal generator and do not increase the output beyond the safe value for the transistor under test. If no output is obtained from the loudspeaker, do not go on increasing the output from the signal generator.

The safe value of the signal generator output will be determined by the emitter base potential of the transistor, but remember that the r.m.s. value of the signal is not the important consideration, the full peak amplitude of the a.c. input being applied across the input of the stage. The half cycles which apply forward bias are those which are important, but this does not affect the calculation of the safe test potential.

Now we can proceed to the examples on the transistorized superhet receiver. The circuit for this receiver is given at the end of the program, and you should unfold this so that it can be seen whichever page you are using.

Turn to *Frame 306* for the first example.

305

Correct. You would inject a test signal to the gain control, thus half-splitting the possible faulty area. This is also a point in the receiver which is very easy to find and is very easy to inject a signal to, which is not always the case in printed circuit construction.

Remember to take care that the injected signal is not too large.

The result of this test is that there is no output in the loud-speaker.

What should be your next step?

A. Inject a test signal to the loudspeaker   *Frame 308*
B. Inject a test signal to the base of transistor G4   *Frame 310*
C. Inject a test signal to the base of transistor G5   *Frame 313*

TRANSISTOR PROBLEM NO.1

Here is the first transistor circuit fault.

When the receiver is switched on there is no output on either waveband.

What should be the first move?

    A. Listen for hum in the loudspeaker   *Frame 307*
    B. Listen for a click in the loudspeaker when the receiver is switched on   *Frame 309*
    C. Check to see if the pilot lamp is on   *Frame 311*

307

Your answer was that you would listen for hum in the loudspeaker. Although this would be the correct move in a valve receiver it is not the best move in a transistorized receiver. In the valve receiver the hum we listened for was produced by the mains ripple on the h.t. supply. In this circuit we do not use a mains supply, and this hum would not be present.

In a transistorized receiver the easiest way of checking the probability of the audio stages being correct is to listen for a click in the loudspeaker when the set is switched on. This is produced by the transient voltage of the supply as it rises over a very short period to its maximum value.

Turn to *Frame 309.*

308

You said that you would now inject a test signal to the loud-speaker. This is not correct as this point is not the mid-point of the faulty area. Moreover, this would be checking a single component and you have been taught not to do this at this stage of the fault-finding method.

When a test signal was injected to the gain control there was no output from the loudspeaker. Therefore, the faulty area is the whole of the receiver after the gain control. The next test point must be the mid-point of this faulty area.

Try the question again.

Turn to *Frame 305*.

309

Correct. You should listen for a click in the loudspeaker when the receiver is switched on. This will show whether the d.c. supply is available and whether the audio stages are correct.

This serves the same purpose as listening for hum in the valve superhet produced by the mains ripple on the h.t. supply. In the transistor circuit the transient voltage produced when the receiver is switched on passes through the audio stages as a signal.

In this particular case there is a click when the receiver is switched on.

What should be the next step to help to isolate the fault?

A. Inject a test signal to the gain control   *Frame 305*
B. Inject a test signal to the base of transistor G5   *Frame 312*
C. Inject a test signal to the base of transistor G2   *Frame 314*

310

You said that you would now inject a test signal to the base of the transistor G4. This is not correct as this point is not the mid-point of the faulty area.

When a test signal was injected to the gain control there was no output from the loudspeaker. Therefore, the faulty area is the whole of the receiver after the gain control. The next test point must be the mid-point of this faulty area.

Try the question again.

Turn to *Frame 305*.

311

Checking the pilot lamp to see if the supply is available is a very good move if a pilot lamp is fitted. However, if you had looked more carefully at this circuit you would have noticed that there is not a pilot lamp fitted.

Pilot lamps are not normally fitted in transistorized circuits as the current drain of the lamp would be of the order of the drain on the battery of the circuit, and this would considerably shorten the battery life. The total current drain of this receiver is approximately 30 milliamps.

Hence, another method of checking whether the supply is available must be found.

Turn to *Frame 306* and try the question again.

312

Your answer was that you would inject a test signal to the base of the transistor G5. This is half-splitting the audio frequency stages and is not correct. There is no evidence so far that the audio frequency stages contain the fault. The faulty area is still the whole of the receiver.

Carry out the half-split method correctly.

Turn to *Frame 309* and attempt the question again.

313

Correct. The next test should bo to inject a test signal to the base of the transistor G5. This is the mid-point of the faulty area, considering the push-pull amplifier as one stage, even though it contains more than one transistor.

The result of this test is that there is a normal output from the loudspeaker.

What is now the faulty area of the receiver?

A. The power amplifier   *Frame 315*
B. The audio frequency voltage amplifier   *Frame 317*
C. The area before the audio stages   *Frame 319*

314

Your answer was that you would inject a test signal to the base of transistor G2, the first intermediate frequency amplifier. This is not correct.

This would be the correct test point if the audio frequency stages were known definitely to be correct. However, this is not known. The previous test proved only that the supply was present and that the loudspeaker was definitely correct. The audio frequency stages were probably correct, but this was not proved beyond doubt.

Therefore you will have to assume that the fault could lie anywhere in the receiver.

Turn to *Frame 309* and try the question again.

315

No, the power amplifier is not the faulty stage of the receiver. When the test signal was injected to the base of transistor G5, it was injected to the power amplifier. As the output was then normal the power amplifier must be functioning correctly.

The tests carried out so far are as follows:

1. When a test signal was injected to the gain control there was no output
2. When a test signal was injected to the base of transistor G5 there was a normal output.

The fault must therefore lie in the first audio frequency amplifier.

Turn to *Frame 317*.

316

The previous tests isolated the fault to between the gain control and the base of transistor G5. This is then the possible faulty area. To further split this faulty area by signal injection, you should inject to the mid-point of the area. The junction of resistor R12 and resistor R13 is not the mid-point.

Work out the position of this mid-point, and then answer the question again.

Turn to *Frame 320*.

317

Your answer was correct. The fault must lie in the audio frequency voltage amplifier stage.

Now that the fault has been isolated to one stage, is there any more signal injection which can be performed?

    A. Yes *Frame 320*
    B. No *Frame 322*

318

The previous test isolated the fault to between the gain control and the base of transistor G5. This is then the possible faulty area. To further split this area by signal injection, you shoulc inject to the mid-point of the area. The collector of transistor G4 is not the mid-point, and is in fact connected directly to the base of transistor G5.

Work out the position of this mid-point, and then answer the question again.

Turn to *Frame 320*.

319

No, the fault does not lie in the area of the receiver before the audio frequency stages. When a test signal was injected to the gain control there was no output from the loudspeaker. Therefore the fault must lie after the gain control, and it must be somewhere in the audio frequency stages.

Now try the question again.

Turn to *Frame 313*.

320

Correct. Signal injection can often be most useful in a faulty stage. This is especially so in transistorized equipment employing the printed circuit type of construction. In these cases it is often very difficult to carry out resistance checks properly, due to the difficulty of disconnecting a component from the printed circuit board. Signal injection, however, can easily be carried out if the correct terminals are fitted to the signal generator.

Assuming that you are going to pursue signal injection further, what should be the next step in isolating the fault?

- A. Inject a test signal to the junction of resistor R13 and resistor R12   *Frame 316*
- B. Inject a test signal to the collector of transistor G4 *Frame 318*
- C. Inject a test signal to the base of transistor G4   *Frame 323*

321

Compare your list of faulty components with the following list.

The possible faulty components are resistor R13, resistor R12, potentiometer RV, capacitor C15 or capacitor C16.

In fact, resistor R12 or resistor R13 or capacitor C16 should be on open circuit, or resistor RV or capacitor C15 should be on short circuit.

How are you going to discover the actual faulty component?

A. Measure the resistance of each component   *Frame 325*
B. Measure the resistance to earth from the junction of resistor R12 and resistor R13   *Frame 326*
C. Inject a test signal to the junction of resistor R12 and resistor R13   *Frame 328*

322

You said that signal injection could not be carried any further once the faulty stage had been isolated. This is not completely correct. There are occasions when it will be extremely useful to extend signal injection into a faulty stage.

Turn to *Frame 320*.

323

Correct. The previous tests isolated the fault to between the gain control and the base of transistor G5. Injecting a test signal to the base of transistor G4 would conveniently half-split this area.

The result of this test is that the output is now normal.

Make a list of the possible faulty components.

When you have done this, turn to *Frame 321*.

TRANSISTOR PROBLEM NO.2

Now we can go on to the second problem on the transistorized superhet receiver. Remember that the basic method of fault finding is exactly the same for transistorized equipment as for valve equipment, and in fact the method can be applied to any equipment.

The second fault is as follows:

When the receiver is tuned to a known signal, the output is found to be very weak. Other receivers are producing a normal output from the same signal.

What should be your first step in isolating the fault?

    A.   Check the battery voltage   *Frame 327*
    B.   Tune to other radio stations   *Frame 329*
    C.   Turn up the gain control   *Frame 331*

325

Your answer was that you would measure the resistance of each component on the list. This would come up with the faulty component fairly quickly. However, measuring all these resistances will entail unsoldering at least one contact on each component and this will not be the most efficient method to use. You already have the signal generator set up and it will be easier to move the contact of the generator one place along the circuit, than to carry out resistance measurements.

Turn to *Frame 328*.

326

Your answer was that you would measure the resistance to earth from the junction of resistor R12 and resistor R13. This would be correct if resistance measurements were the most efficient at this point. However, there is a more efficient method of isolating the fault. This is to carry on with signal injection. As the signal generator is already set up all you would have to do would be to move one contact of the generator output to the next test point.

Turn to *Frame 328*.

327

Your answer was that you would check the battery voltage. This is not correct. Although this could be the fault we are looking for, the receiver chassis would have to be removed from the case, and a special test carried out in order to check the battery. There is a much simpler move which does not entail stripping the receiver or specialized tests and which will provide valuable information on the fault.

Remember that the first step in fault finding is symptom analysis, and if you do not have sufficient symptoms immediately available, you must obtain further symptoms by the use of the controls or by any other convenient means.

Bearing this in mind, what would be the correct first step in isolating the fault?

A. Tune to other radio stations   *Frame 330*
B. Turn up the gain control   *Frame 335*

Correct. You would inject a test signal to the junction of resistor R12 and resistor R13. This would half-split the faulty area. It is easier to carry on with signal injection as the generator is already set up, and no unsoldering would have to be done as it would to take resistance measurements of individual components. The result of this test is that there is no output from the loudspeaker.

The fault must now be either a short circuit in capacitor C15, or an open circuit in resistor R12 or capacitor C16.

Having narrowed down the fault to these three components, there is no particular advantage in testing any of them before the others. The fault actually chosen for this example was that the capacitor C15 contained a short circuit.

You have now completed the first problem on the transistor circuit, and you should have found that there is no major difference between the method used for this fault and the method used for the valve circuit faults. This should be so, as the method this program teaches is a basic method of fault finding which can be applied to any equipment. There are a few special points to consider in transistorized circuits, but the basic principles are exactly the same, whatever type of equipment is used.

Now turn to *Frame 333* for the second example on the transistorized superhet receiver (circuit at the end of the program).

Your answer was that you would tune to other radio stations. This would provide you with other information concerning the fault, and would be part of symptom analysis. Moreover, this would only take a few seconds to carry out and therefore it would be a useful move.

The result of this test is that all the received signals are weak.

What should be your next step?

A. Check the battery voltage *Frame 332*
B. Turn up the gain control *Frame 337*

330

You said that you would first of all tune to other radio stations. This is correct. The result of this test will provide information concerning the fault, and it is correctly carrying out symptom analysis.

The result of this test is that all signals are weak.

However, there is little to choose between tuning to other radio signals and turning up the gain control as the first step. Although this may not be considered to be sensible, it is not in fact wasting time. A surprising number of faults are extremely simple, so simple that they are often overlooked. To turn up the gain control would only take a few seconds, and would provide further information on the fault.

The result of this test is that all signals are still weak.

Turn to *Frame 337*.

331

Your answer was that you would turn up the gain control as the first step in isolating the fault. This is correct.

Although this may not be considered to be a sensible move it is not in fact wasting time. A surprising number of faults are extremely simple, so simple that they are often overlooked. To turn up the gain control would only take a few seconds, and would provide further information on the fault.

The result of this test is that the signal is till weak.

What should be your next step?

A. Check the battery *Frame 334*
B. Tune to other radio stations *Frame 337*

332

As your second step in finding the fault, you said that you would check the battery. This is not correct.

To do this would entail removing the battery, or at least removing the case of the receiver, and carrying out a test on the battery. Although this is a very simple move, and this could very probably be the fault, there is another move which should be taken first. This is to turn up the gain control. Although this may not be considered to be correct, it is certainly not wasting time.

A surprising number of faults are extremely simple, so simple that they are often overlooked. To turn up the gain control would only take a few seconds, and would provide further information on the fault. To do this would be carrying out more symptom analysis, which is correct.

Turn to *Frame 337*.

333

You have now completed the first problem on the transistorized superhet receiver. It is possible that you have discovered that your knowledge of transistor theory is inadequate for these problems. If so, do not attempt to work through the subsequent transistor problems, and turn to *Frame 382*.

If you have discovered that your knowledge of transistor theory is adequate, but you have forgotten parts of the fault-finding method, revise this method from the *flow sheet* at the end of the program before continuing.

If you wish to proceed directly to the second transistor problem, turn to *Frame 324*.

334

As your second step in finding the fault, you said that you would check the battery. This is not correct.

To do this would entail removing the battery, or at least removing the case of the receiver, and carrying out a test on the battery. Although this is a simple move, and this could very probably be the fault, there is another move which should be taken first. This is to tune to other radio stations and check the receiver output. This would take a very short while, would not entail removing the receiver case, and would give relevant information on the fault. To do this would be carrying out more symptom analysis, which is correct.

Turn to *Frame 337*.

335

You said that you would first of all turn up the gain control. This is correct. A surprising number of faults are extremely simple and are often overlooked because of this. The result of this test will provide information concerning the fault, and it is correctly carrying out symptom analysis.

The result of this test is that signals are still weak.

The next step should then be to tune to other radio stations and check the receiver output, taking symptom analysis a stage further.

The result of this test is that all signals are still weak.

Neither of these moves entailed any special tests, and their results, considered together, would provide valuable information concerning the fault.

Always pursue symptom analysis as far as possible, before carrying out any other tests. Any move taken as part of this symptom analysis will be very simple, and will only take a very short time.

Now turn to *Frame 337*.

336

Good. The next test signal should be injected to the mid-point of the faulty area. As the faulty area had been narrowed down to the stages before the audio frequency stages, the next test signal should be injected to the base of the intermediate frequency transistor G2.

The result of this test is that the output is very weak when the correct input is applied. What should be the next step?

A. Carry out voltage and resistance checks in the intermediate frequency stages   *Frame 342*
B. Inject a test signal to the base of transistor G3   *Frame 344*
C. Inject a test signal to the second detector   *Frame 346*

337

The information gained so far is that the gain control has little effect upon the low output, and tuning to other radio stations does not improve the output of the receiver.

It would now be wise to check the battery voltage before proceeding any further. Although this step does not agree with the order of the method which you have been taught, it is now a very possible fault, and one which should be checked now before going on to signal injection and the other steps. Whatever the next step was, it would entail removing the chassis from the receiver case, and this would make it very simple to check the battery. Remember that the battery should be checked on load.

The result of this test is that the battery is found to provide the normal supply, and therefore this is not the fault we have been looking for. In fact, a low battery voltage often produces distortion of the output as well as a low output, and this was not observed in this case.

Equipment inspection shows no obvious faults.

What should be the next step in the fault-finding method?

A. Inject a test signal to the intermediate frequency stages   *Frame 339*
B. Inject a test signal to the aerial   *Frame 341*
C. Inject a test signal to the audio frequency stages   *Frame 343*

338

Your answer was that you would inject a test signal to the base of transistor G3. This is a reasonable answer, but is not completely correct. You are splitting the faulty area by this move, but a better move would be to split the faulty area by injecting a test signal to the base of transistor G2.

Turn to *Frame 336*.

339

Your answer was that you would inject a test signal to the intermediate frequency stages. This is not correct.

The results you have obtained so far have not isolated the fault to any particular area of the receiver. Therefore the first test signal should be injected to the mid-point of the complete receiver. This point is the input of the audio frequency stages, and this is where the first test signal should be injected.

Turn to *Frame 343*.

340

No, your answer is not correct. When the test signal was injected to the audio frequency stages, and the output was found to be normal, the faulty area was proved to be the area of the receiver before the audio frequency stages. The next test signal must half-split this faulty area.

Work out the mid-point of the area of the receiver before the audio frequency stages, and then answer the question on *Frame 343* again.

341

Your answer was that you would inject a test signal to the aerial. This is not correct.

You should never inject to the beginning of a faulty area, always at the mid-point. Injecting to the aerial would give no new information concerning the fault. The only possible reason for doing this would be if the signal was suspected, rather than the receiver. However, in this case all signals received were weak, not just one, and other receivers were operating normally.

Now turn to *Frame 337* and give the correct answer.

342

Your answer was that you would carry out voltage and resistance checks in the intermediate frequency stages. This is not correct. The fault has not yet been isolated to one single stage, and therefore voltage and resistance checks should not yet be used.

Signal injection must be pursued until the fault is isolated to one single stage.

Turn to *Frame 336* and make another attempt at the question.

343

Correct. The fault can only be assumed to lie somewhere in the receiver, the tests so far failing to isolate one probable faulty area. Therefore the test signal should be injected to the mid-point of the receiver.

The result of this test is that the output signal is now at normal strength with the correct value of input to the test point.

What should be the next step?

A. Inject a test signal to the base of the intermediate frequency transistor G2 *Frame 336*
B. Inject a test signal to the base of the intermediate frequency transistor G3 *Frame 338*
C. Inject a test signal to the base of the mixer transistor G1 *Frame 340*

344

Correct. The next test should be to inject a test signal to the base of the transistor G3. This is half-splitting the faulty area.

The result of this test is that the output is normal.

Has this isolated the fault to one stage?

A. Yes *Frame 347*
B. No *Frame 349*

345

Correct. In transistorized circuits, it is often easier to pursue signal injection than to carry out voltage and resistance checks. The correct point of injection will be the mid-point of the faulty area, in this case the first intermediate frequency amplifier, and the mid-point will be the collector of transistor G2.

The result of injecting a test signal to this point is that the output is now normal.

This isolates the fault to be within the first intermediate frequency amplifier, before the collector of the transistor G2, and the fault is such that it is cutting down the amplification of the amplifier.

Amongst the possible faults are

    (i)   A faulty transistor
   (ii)   Excessive a.v.c. voltage
  (iii)   Incorrect base voltage.

Which of these three possible faults do you consider should be checked first?

   A.   (i)   *Frame 348*
   B.   (ii)   *Frame 351*
   C.   (iii)   *Frame 353*

346

Your answer was that you would inject a test signal to the second detector. This would narrow the faulty area but it would be more efficient to inject a test signal to the base of the transistor G3.

Turn to *Frame 344*.

347

Yes. The two previous tests bracketed the first intermediate frequency amplifier, and the fault must lie in this stage.

Now what should be the next step in isolating the fault?

    A. Inject a test signal to the collector of the transistor G2
        Frame 345
    B. Carry out voltage and resistance checks in the first intermediate frequency stage   *Frame 350*

348

Your answer was that the first check should be to examine the transistor to determine by testing it whether it is faulty. This is a possible fault, but it should not be carried out as the first check. Disconnecting the transistor and carrying out tests in a transistor tester, or replacing the transistor by another good one, will not be particularly quick or easy. Always attempt to carry out the easiest, quickest test first when there is a choice of tests.

In this case there was a much easier test which would eliminate a fault just as possible as a faulty transistor.

Bearing this in mind, attempt the question again.

Turn to *Frame 345*.

349

You said that the fault had not yet been isolated to one stage. This is not correct.

When a test signal was injected to the base of transistor G3 the output was normal, and when the test signal was injected to the base of transistor G2 the output was weak. Therefore the fault must lie in the first intermediate frequency stage.

Turn to *Frame 347*.

350

Your answer was that once the fault had been isolated to one stage, the next step would be to carry out voltage and resistance checks in that stage.

According to the method which you learnt earlier in the program, this would be the correct step. However, in the earlier example on fault finding in transistorized circuits, you were told that it was often easier to pursue signal injection beyond finding the faulty stage. For the purpose of this example, assume that it is in fact easier to pursue signal injection into the faulty stage.

Turn to *Frame 345*.

351

Most probably the best item to be checked first is the a.v.c. voltage. An excessive value of the feedback a.v.c. could produce the symptoms which have been given. The other possible faults given could also produce these symptoms, but the a.v.c. would be easiest to check, and should therefore be checked first of all.

The a.v.c. supply is fed through resistor R7, and the best test point would be the junction of resistor R7 and capacitor C6. When the voltage is checked at this point it is found to be 0·7 volt.

Is the a.v.c. supply excessive?

A. Yes   *Frame 354*
B. No   *Frame 356*

352

Your answer was that you would replace the transistor G2. This is not correct. Although this is a possible fault, you should not replace components until you are more certain that they are faulty. In this case there are other tests which could be carried out on the faulty stage, and which would provide more positive proof of the actual fault.

Turn to *Frame 356* and attempt the question again.

353

Your answer was that the first check should be to examine the transistor base voltage. This is a possible fault, and could be checked very easily. However, the most likely reason for incorrect base voltage in this stage would be incorrect a.v.c. feedback, therefore this should be checked first.

The transistor should not be checked at this point until further voltage and resistance checks have shown that there is a further possibility of the transistor being at fault.

Turn to *Frame 351*.

354

Your answer was that the a.v.c. voltage was probably excessive. This is not correct.

The voltage measured at the test point of the junction of the resistor R7 and the capacitor C6 was 0·7 volt, and the correct base voltage is given as 0·8 volt. As the only resistance between the test point and the base is the secondary winding of the transformer IF1, and this will be small, there should be very little potential difference between the base and the test point. Therefore the voltage is probably correct, allowing for tolerance limits.

Turn to *Frame 356*.

355

Your answer was that you would measure the emitter to chassis voltage. However, this should have been carried out as part of the previous step, when all voltages around the transistor were measured. You must keep clear in your mind which steps have been performed. Remember that a list will often prove useful, especially with the more difficult faults.

Your answer should have been a measurement which would provide further information on the fault.

Turn to *Frame 360* and see if you can give an answer which will provide more information on the fault.

356

Correct. As the base voltage of the transistor G2 is given as 0·8 volt, the value of 0·7 volt for the junction of resistor R7 and capacitor C6 is a reasonable value, and it could be assumed from this that the a.v.c. feedback is not excessive. This has eliminated one possible fault.

What should be the next step?

- A. Replace the transistor G2   *Frame 352*
- B. Carry out resistance checks on the faulty stage (the first intermediate frequency amplifier)   *Frame 358*
- C. Carry out voltage checks on the faulty stage (the first intermediate frequency amplifier)   *Frame 360*

357

Right. The next step should be to measure the resistance from the emitter to chassis, as the previous test showed a suspected fault in the emitter circuit.

Remember that special precautions need to be taken when measuring resistance in a transistorized circuit as you were told earlier. The meter should be connected so that it applies reverse bias to the transistor junction, and if possible the transistor should be disconnected at the base to ensure that it will not be damaged, or spurious readings result.

When this resistance is measured, it is found to be 695 kilohms. This measurement has isolated the fault, as it would appear that the resistance R5 has been incorrectly inserted in the receiver at some time. The correct value of the resistor is 680 ohms, and obviously a 695 kilohm resistor has been inserted by mistake.

This fault should not occur under normal conditions, but is the type of fault which could occur on assembly and be missed by a visual check.

Once again, the fault-finding method should be seen to be exactly similar in basic steps to the fault-finding method which can be applied to valve equipment, and the method can, in fact, be applied to any type of electronic equipment.

Now turn to *Frame 361* for the third example on fault finding in the transistorized superhet circuit.

358

Your answer was that you would now carry out resistance checks on the faulty stage. This would provide further information on the fault, but you would probably find it a little easier and more efficient if you carried out voltage checks before resistance checks.

Turn to *Frame 360*.

359

Your answer was that as the emitter-base voltage was found to be too low, you would measure the resistance from the base to chassis. In normal circumstances this would be correct. However, in an earlier test you investigated the circuit between the base and chassis when the a.v.c. line was checked. As the result of this showed that there was no suspected fault in the base circuit, then you should have measured the resistance from emitter to chassis for this test, rather than base to chassis resistance.

Turn to *Frame 357*.

360

Correct. The next step is to measure the voltages of the faulty stage, the first intermediate frequency amplifier. The first voltages measured should be the collector, base and emitter voltages of the transistor G2. In fact the base voltage has already had a preliminary check, when the a.v.c. voltage was measured. Remember that when the a.v.c. voltage is checked, special precautions are necessary with regard to input signal and gain control.

Suppose that when the collector, base and emitter voltages are measured, the emitter-base voltage is found to be too low, and the other voltages are correct.

What should be the next step?

A. Check the emitter to chassis voltage   *Frame 355*
B. Check the resistance from emitter to chassis   *Frame 357*
C. Check the resistance from the base to chassis   *Frame 359*

TRANSISTOR PROBLEM NO.3

Here is the third example on the transistorized superhet receiver whose circuit is given at the end of the program.

The fault is that the output from the receiver is low and signals are distorted. It is extremely unlikely that any result would be obtained from equipment inspection in this case, and you can assume that no fault is noticed when equipment inspection is carried out.

What should be the first step in attempting to isolate this fault?

A. Vary the setting of the gain control *Frame 363*
B. Check the battery *Frame 365*
C. Tune to another signal *Frame 367*

362

Your answer was that you would now carry out equipment inspection. This is the correct move after symptom analysis, but you were told on the first frame of this problem that no result could be obtained from this test.

Turn to *Frame 371* and answer the question again, assuming that equipment inspection has been completed.

363

You said that the first step should be to vary the setting of the gain control. This will obtain further symptoms concerning the fault. However, the gain control is found to operate normally, apart from the low level of the signal, and the distortion is still present, with no evidence that it is produced before or after the gain control.

What should be your next step?

A. Check the battery *Frame 364*
B. Tune to another signal *Frame 368*

364

You said that the next step should be to check the battery. This is not correct. Although the symptoms do point towards this as being a possible fault, all obtainable symptoms should be gathered before checking an individual component. You should therefore alter the setting of the gain control and alter the tuning to discover all possible symptoms.

Having done this, the battery would now be a reasonable item to suspect, since the gain control and the tuning did not produce any new symptoms. The gain control was found to operate normally, and the symptoms were present on all signals. However, when the battery is checked, it is found to have a normal potential on load.

Turn to *Frame 371*.

365

Your answer was that you would check the battery.

In this case the symptoms do point towards this as being a possible fault. You were told earlier that if the battery potential was low, the output would be low and distorted. However, it would most probably be more correct to press on with symptom analysis first, by varying the setting of the gain control and tuning to another signal, before carrying out a specific test on the battery. Both of these moves would only take a few seconds and would not be wasting time.

The result of these two steps is that the gain control is found to operate normally, apart from the low level of the signal, and the distortion is still present, with exactly the same effect being noted on each signal.

Having done this, the battery would now be a reasonable item to suspect and it could be checked. However, when this is done, the battery potential on load is found to be normal.

Turn to *Frame 371*.

366

Correct. The first step of symptom analysis has been completed, and the second step of equipment inspection can be taken as complete because you were told that, in this problem, no information could be gained from this step. The next move is then to carry out signal injection or signal tracing, and in this case signal injection will be more useful.

The fault has not been isolated to any particular area of the receiver, and therefore the first test signal should be injected to the mid-point of the receiver which is the base of the transistor G4.

The result of this test is that the output is now normal.

What should be your next move?

A. Inject a test signal to the base of transistor G5
   Frame 370
B. Inject a test signal to the base of transistor G3
   Frame 372
C. Inject a test signal to the base of transistor G2
   Frame 374

367

You said that the first step should be to vary the setting of the tuning and tune to another signal. This will obtain further symptoms concerning the fault. However, the symptoms of low output and distortion are found to occur on all received signals.

What should be your next step?

A. Check the battery   *Frame 364*
B. Vary the setting of the gain control   *Frame 368*

368

Correct. Before carrying out checks on individual components, such as the battery, all possible symptoms should be obtained and considered collectively.

The gain control can be varied, and the tuning altered to discover any new symptoms.

The result of these two steps is that the gain control is found to operate normally, apart from the low level of the signal, and the distortion is still present, with exactly the same effect being noted on each signal.

Having done this, the battery would now be a reasonable item to suspect and it could be checked. However, when this is done, the battery potential on load is found to be normal.

Turn to *Frame 371*.

369

No. Voltage checks should not be carried out at this stage. You must follow the method of fault finding which has been taught. If you are not certain of the order of the steps, turn to the revision sheet at the end of the program.

When you have done this, turn to *Frame 371* and answer the question again.

370

No. Injecting a test signal to the base of transistor G5 would be a complete waste of time. When the test signal was injected to the base of transistor G4 the output was normal, and therefore all stages after this point must be correct. Therefore the stage containing transistor G5 has already been proved to be correct.

The previous test proved that the fault must lie before the base of transistor G4.

Turn to *Frame 366* and answer the question again.

371

At this point, symptom analysis has not produced an estimate of the fault, and it could still be anywhere in the receiver.

What should be your next move?

A. Carry out equipment inspection *Frame 362*
B. Inject a test signal to the base of the audio transistor G4 *Frame 366*
C. Carry out voltage checks *Frame 369*

372

Your answer was that the next test would be to inject a test signal to tho base of the transistor G3. This is partly correct.

The previous test proved that the fault lay before the base of transistor G4, and the next test must then further isolate the faulty stage. However, following the half-split method, it would be better to inject the test signal to the base of the transistor G2, as this would isolate the fault more quickly.

Turn to *Frame 374*.

373

Your answer was that you would carry out voltage and resistance checks on the mixer stage. Although this is the next step in the fault-finding method, you were told that it is often easier in transistorized circuits to pursue signal injection beyond the point of determining the faulty stage.

In this case you should go on with signal injection, so turn to *Frame 378* and answer the question again.

374

Correct. The previous test isolated the fault to before the base of the transistor G4, and injecting a test signal to the base of transistor G2 is half-splitting the faulty area. Always use the half-split method if at all possible, as it will isolate the fault more efficiently.

The result of this test is that the output is normal.

What should be the next step in isolating the fault?

    A. Inject a test signal to the aerial socket   *Frame 376*
    B. Inject a test signal to the base of transistor G1   *Frame 378*
    C. Carry out voltage checks in the stage containing the transistor G1   *Frame 380*

375

Your answer was that you would inject a test signal to the aerial socket. This is not correct.

You would obtain no new information from this test as the tests carried out so far have proved that the fault lies after the base of the transistor G1. Moreover, this would nearly always be an incorrect move, as injecting to the input of the receiver will simply confirm that there is a fault in the receiver, a fact which is already known.

Turn to *Frame 378* and answer the question correctly.

376

Your answer was that you would now inject a test signal to the aerial socket. This is not correct.

The tests so far have proved that the fault lies before the base of the transistor G2. Injecting a test signal to the aerial socket would provide no new information concerning the fault as the output is bound to be distorted and low, and this is known already. The fault could not be in the signal itself, since symptom analysis proved that the fault occurred on all signals.
You must carry on with the half-split method.

Turn to *Frame 374* and attempt the question again.

377

You said that you would now replace the mixer/oscillator transformer. Although this is almost certainly the faulty component, it would not be a completely correct move to replace it immediately because this would be a fairly complicated procedure involving re-alignment. It would be better to be absolutely certain of the fault before committing yourself to this replacement. You should therefore check the resistance of the 5/6 winding of the mixer/oscillator transformer before replacing it.

The resistance of this winding, with the transformer disconnected, is found to be infinity, and there is therefore an open circuit on the 5/6 winding.

The transformer can now be replaced.

Turn to *Frame 383*.

378

Correct. You should carry on with the half-split method of signal injection, and the next test point should be the base of transistor G1.

In the valve superhet, it was found most convenient when injecting to the mixer stage to inject the intermediate frequency as the test frequency, since this would check the mixer stage without unnecessary complications from the local oscillator. In the transistorized superhet receiver, the same consideration applies, and the test frequency to be injected to the base of the transistor G1 should be the intermediate frequency, which for this receiver is 470 kHz.

The result of this test is that the output is low and distorted.

What should be the next step?

- A. Carry out voltage and resistance checks on the mixer stage *Frame 373*
- B. Inject a test signal to the aerial socket *Frame 375*
- C. Inject a test signal to the collector of the transistor G1 *Frame 381*

379

Your answer was that you should measure the voltage across the 5/6 winding of the mixer/oscillator transformer. This is not correct and would provide no useful information at this stage.

Turn to *Frame 381* and give the correct answer.

380

Your answer was that you would carry out voltage checks in the mixer stage. Although this is partly correct, as signal injection has narrowed down the fault to one stage, it would not be a particularly convenient move as the area of the fault is still very large. It would be more convenient in this case, as in most transistor circuits, to pursue signal injection to sub-stage levels, and the next step should therefore be to inject a test signal to the base of the transistor G1.

Turn to *Frame 378*.

381

Correct. You should carry on with signal injection, progressively narrowing the faulty area, and the next test point should be the collector of the transistor G1. In fact, the most convenient injection point would be across the primary winding of the mixer/oscillator transformer, the winding 5/6.

The result of this test injection is that the output is still low and distorted.

It will now be a very simple move to inject a test signal to the primary winding of the first intermediate frequency transformer IF1, as the signal generator is already set up to give this frequency.

When the test signal is injected to the winding 1/2 of the transformer IF1, the output is normal.

What should be your next step?

A. Replace the mixer/oscillator transformer   *Frame 377*
B. Measure the voltage across the 5/6 winding of the mixer/oscillator transformer   *Frame 379*
C. Measure the resistance across the 5/6 winding of the mixer/oscillator transformer   *Frame 382*

382

Correct. The resistance of the 5/6 winding of the mixer/oscillator transformer should be checked before the transformer is replaced. Before replacing this particular component you must be completely certain that it is the faulty one. In this case, performance checks would be particularly important, as part of a tuned circuit has been replaced, and re-alignment would be necessary.

This has now completed the third example on fault finding in the transistorized superhet receiver.

Turn to *Frame 383*.

383

You have now completed this program on systematic fault finding in electronic equipment.

Remember that the method which you have been taught in this program is simply an aid to fault finding and in no way does it substitute for experience or technical knowledge. Those with little experience of fault finding should follow the method implicitly, but as experience is gained short cuts will become allowable. This program is not sufficient in itself to enable fault finding to be pursued efficiently, and the student is advised to consult other work on detailed faults in particular equipments, and also works on electronic measurements and test equipment.

Test 1—Answers

Check your answers to Test 1 against this list. If you are not satisfied with your performance, then work through this section of the program again.

1. Symptom analysis.

2. As many relevant symptoms as possible.

3. Only a few minutes.

4. Only built-in test gear is required.

5. Induced symptoms are obtained by the operation of available controls.

6. Symptom analysis is applied to the whole equipment to determine the faulty unit. It is then applied to the faulty unit to further isolate the fault.

7. Sound electronic theory and an understanding of the principles of the specific equipment under test are vital to correct symptom analysis.

8. The fault lies before the audio stages.

9. The fault probably lies in the a.g.c. circuit.

10. In the radio frequency stages.

When you are satisfied with your answers, turn to *Frame 67* for the next section of the program.

A

Test 2—Answers

Check your answers to Test 2 against this list. If you are not satisfied with your performance, then work through this section of the program again.

1. Equipment inspection.

2. Yes. The chassis must be removed from the case, but only the dismantling required to do this should be carried out at this stage.

3. Only a few minutes.

4. Overheated transformer, faulty valve heater, loose connexion, controls incorrectly set, arcing, damaged resistor.

5. No test equipment is required.

6. Equipment inspection on a multi-unit equipment is carried out first of all on the exterior of the units, and on inter-unit connexions.

7. Only when a certain unit has been proved to contain the fault should equipment inspection be carried out inside a unit.

8. The senses of sight, smell and touch.

When you are satisfied with your answers, turn to *Frame 91* for the next section of the program.

Test 3—Answers

Check your answers to Test 3 against this list. If you are not satisfied with your performance, then work through this section of the program again.

1. Signal injection and signal tracing.

2. To isolate a single faulty stage.

3. A signal generator, with an output meter or oscilloscope.

4. Inject to stage 3.

5. Inject to stage 2.

6. Inject to the first i.f. stage.

7. Inject the i.f. to the mixer.

8. Inject to stage 4.

When you are satisfied with your answers, turn to *Frame 158* for the next section of the program.

Test 4—Answers

Check your answers to Test 4 against this list. If you are not satisfied with your performance, then work through this section of the program again.

1. Voltage and resistance measurements.

2. To isolate a single faulty component in a stage which has previously been proved to be faulty.

3. Only when a stage has been isolated as containing the fault.

4. A voltmeter and an ohmmeter, usually in a multimeter.

5. Voltage measurements should normally be carried out before resistance measurements.

6. A normal a.c. measurement taken during this step is to check the supply to the valve heater.

7. Only when it has been proved to be faulty by voltage and resistance measurements.

8. The cathode voltage will provide most information as to the state of the stage.

9. 10% tolerance should be allowed if no definite limit is stated.

When you are satisfied with your answers, turn to *Frame 203* for the next section of the program.

D

Test 5—Answers

Check your answers to Test 5 against this list. If you are not satisfied with your performance, then work through this section of the program again.

1. Repair and replacement.
2. To repair the previously isolated fault.
3. Only one component should be required to be replaced or repaired, assuming that only one component goes faulty at any one time.
4. No test equipment is required.
5. Performance tests.
6. To check the validity of the repair.
7. Output level, gain, noise level.
8. Fault finding should be repeated from symptom analysis, using the new symptoms of unsatisfactory performance.
9. Immediately after repair.
10. Only if the equipment appears to be functioning correctly, and it is required to operate it urgently.

When you are satisfied with your answers, turn to Frame 210 which leads into the first example on the valve superhet receiver whose circuit diagram is given at the end of the book on a folded inset.

Useful Reading

Radio Theory

A First Course in Wireless	"Decibel"	Pitman	London 1960
Foundations of Wireless	M. G. Scroggie	Iliffe	London 1958
The Superheterodyne Receiver	A. T. Witts	Pitman	London 1961
Radio Communication	J. Reyner and P. Reyner	Pitman	London 1966

Semiconductor Theory

Principles of Semiconductors	M. G. Scroggie	Iliffe	London 1961

Test Equipment

A.C./D.C. Test Meters	W. H. Cazaly and T. Roddam	Pitman	London 1951
Cathode Ray Oscillographs	J. H. Reyner	Pitman	London 1957
Practical Oscilloscope Handbook	R. P. Turner	Iliffe	London 1965

Servicing

Troubleshooting with the Oscilloscope	R. G. Middleton	Foulsham-Sams	Slough 1962
Electrical Measurements and the Calculation of the Errors involved	D. Karo	MacDonald	London 1961
Fundamentals of Radio Receiver Servicing	E. M. Squire	Pitman	London 1961
Radio Upkeep and Repairs	A. T. Witts	Pitman	London 1963
Electronic Measurements	Terman and Pettit	McGraw-Hill	New York 1952

These are necessarily at many different levels, as this program is equally suitable to all levels of servicing personnel. Only a simplified explanation is necessary as a beginning, but those at a higher level will gain just as much benefit from the program.

F